£2.65

Printed and Published in Great Britain by D. C. THOMSON & CO., LTD., 185 Fleet St., London EC4A 2HS.

ISBN 0 85116 361 0

Bunty FOR GIRLS
1987

Robina Hood
IN Sherwood Forest long ago, Robina Hood and her friends, all descendants of Robin Hood and his merry men, set out to continue the noble deeds of their elderly outlaw relatives.
GADZOOKS! 'TIS A ROBBERS' AMBUSH!
YOU ARE THE ROBBERS, FOR IN THOSE BAGS ARE THE TAXES TAKEN FROM THE POOR TO PAY THE RICH!
TAKE THEIR ILL-GOTTEN GAINS, LITTLE JANE!
'TIS ALWAYS A PLEASURE TO TAX THE TAX-COLLECTORS, ROBINA!
THE SHERIFF OF NOTTINGHAM SHALL HEAR OF THIS!
PRAY CONVEY OUR GREETINGS BOTH TO HIM AND ALAN DALE, HIS DEPUTY!
THE BAGS CONTAIN MOSTLY PENNIES. WHAT A MEAGRE HAUL!
PENNIES PERHAPS, FLO TUCK, BUT TO THE PEASANTS WHO PAID THEM, 'TIS A FORTUNE!

Suddenly —
HAVE AT YOU, FOREST FELONS!
WHAT'S THIS — A KNIGHT IN ARMOUR — AND ON THE ATTACK!
SHOOT AWAY HIS SWORD, WINNIE SCARLET!
CLANNG!
YOUR MACE WILL NOT BE PUT TO WORK, EITHER! OFF YOUR HORSE, YOU KNAVE!
NOW, SIR KNIGHT — FORSOOTH, 'TIS BUT A LAD!
AND YOU A FAIR YOUNG DAMSEL!
CAN YOU NOT SEE THAT WE ARE ALL FAIR DAMSELS?
THIS HELMET VISOR BLURS MY SIGHT. I MISTOOK YOU FOR OUTLAWS ROBBING TWO TRAVELLERS.

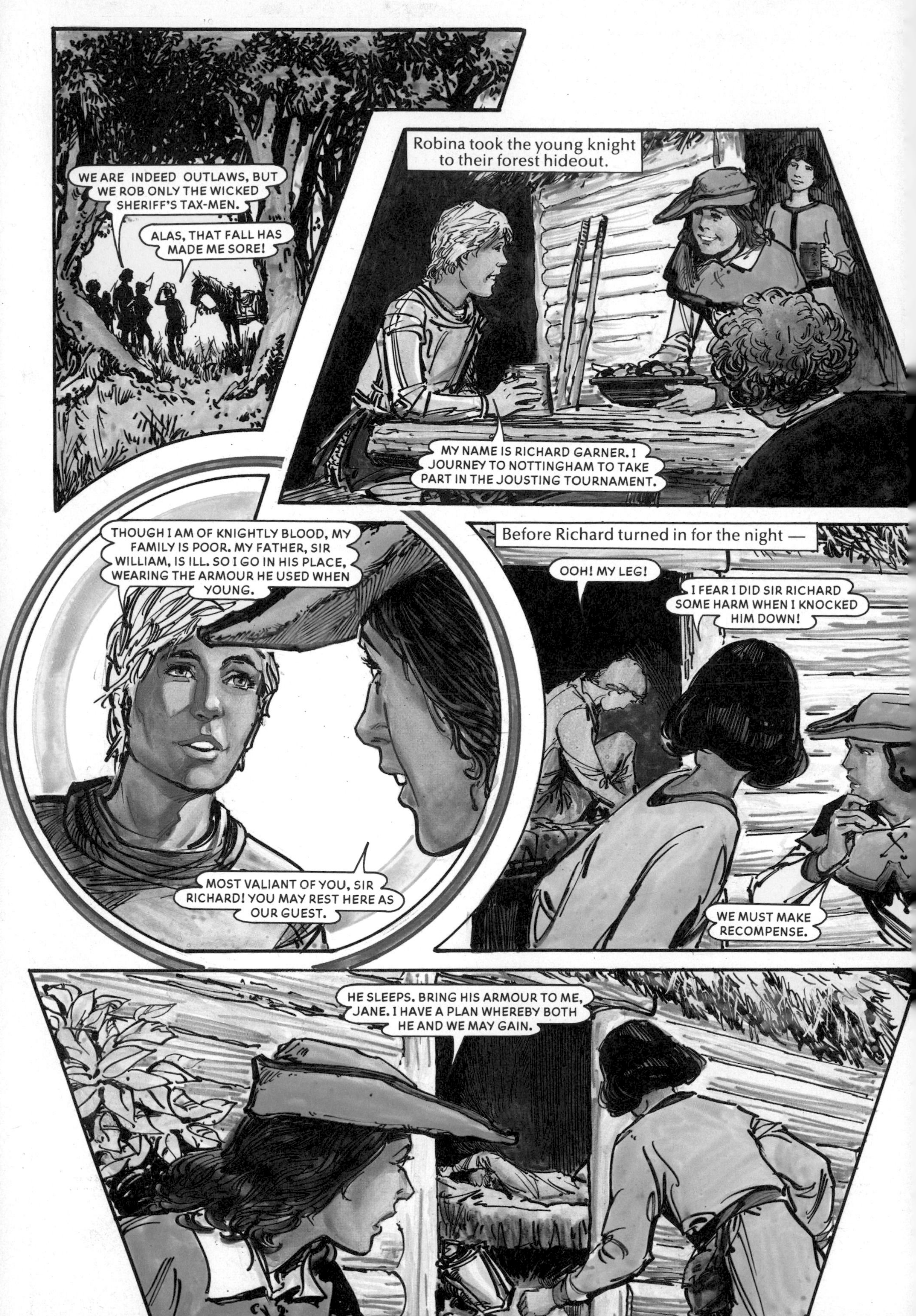
WE ARE INDEED OUTLAWS, BUT WE ROB ONLY THE WICKED SHERIFF'S TAX-MEN.
ALAS, THAT FALL HAS MADE ME SORE!
Robina took the young knight to their forest hideout.
MY NAME IS RICHARD GARNER. I JOURNEY TO NOTTINGHAM TO TAKE PART IN THE JOUSTING TOURNAMENT.
THOUGH I AM OF KNIGHTLY BLOOD, MY FAMILY IS POOR. MY FATHER, SIR WILLIAM, IS ILL. SO I GO IN HIS PLACE, WEARING THE ARMOUR HE USED WHEN YOUNG.
MOST VALIANT OF YOU, SIR RICHARD! YOU MAY REST HERE AS OUR GUEST.
Before Richard turned in for the night —
OOH! MY LEG!
I FEAR I DID SIR RICHARD SOME HARM WHEN I KNOCKED HIM DOWN!
WE MUST MAKE RECOMPENSE.
HE SLEEPS. BRING HIS ARMOUR TO ME, JANE. I HAVE A PLAN WHEREBY BOTH HE AND WE MAY GAIN.

And soon, at old Robin Hood's hideout —
TO ARMS, FRIAR TUCK! A KNIGHT IS ON THE ATTACK!
YOUR BACK IS BENT LIKE YOUR BOW, ROBIN, AND MY OLD LEGS ARE TOO FEEBLE FOR A FIGHT!
'TIS ONLY I, GRANDSIRE ROBIN!
ROBINA! SHAME ON YOU FOR GIVING US SUCH A FRIGHT!
Robina explained what she meant to do —
NOW WILL YOU INSTRUCT ME IN THE ARTS OF JOUSTING AND SWORD PLAY?
SO 'TIS YOUR INTENT TO TAKE THIS YOUNG KNIGHT'S PLACE AT THE NOTTINGHAM TOURNAMENT!
So for the next few hours —
LET YOUR STEED PRANCE TO EVADE THE OTHER KNIGHT'S LANCE!
OFF WITH ITS HEAD!
PHEW! THIS IS A WEIGHTY BLADE!

On her return, Robina explained her plan to Richard. Next morning —
YOU TAKE A RISK ACCOMPANYING ME HERE LIKE THIS, JANE.
DISGUISED IN GOWNS, OUR WEAPONS HIDDEN IN THE CART, WE ARE SCARCE LIKELY TO BE ESPIED BY THE SHERIFF AND HIS MEN.
TAKE CARE, ALL THE SAME.
So the tournament began —
THE DUKE OF HARFORD PRESIDES TODAY. HE HAS A FOREIGN GUEST, THE PRINCE OF ARAGON WHO ENTERS HIS SPANISH CHAMPION. HE IS A MUCH-FEARED KNIGHT!
I BEGIN TO THINK MY BOLD NOTION IS ALL A SAD MISTAKE!
OOOH! AAGH!
GADZUMPS! SUCH FEARFUL BUMPS!
HAVE WE NOT MET BEFORE, SIR RICHARD?
NAY, I THINK NOT!
'TIS ALAN DALE, DEPUTY SHERIFF! I'D BEST CLOSE MY VISOR AND ENTER THE RING.

SIR RICHARD GARNER ENTERS FOR THE FREE-FOR-ALL COMBAT! LAST KNIGHT STILL ON HIS FEET GAINS THE PRIZE!
CARAMBA! HAVE AT YOU!
SAINTS PRESERVE ME! 'TIS DON DEMONIO, THE SPANISH CHAMPION! PRANCE, STEED, AS GRANDSIRE ROBIN ADVISED!
OOOF!
THE RUSE WORKED WELL! I SCORED A HIT!
But then —
BE OFF! NOW FIGHT ON FOOT!
OOH!
Next moment —
KERBLANNG!
AGH! WHAT A BLOW — I AM UNDONE!

A FAIR YOUNG MAID!
SIR RICHARD'S ANCIENT ARMOUR WAS TOO FEEBLE TO WITHSTAND SUCH A HIT! WHAT WILL HAPPEN NOW?
I KNEW IT, UNCLE! YONDER YOUNG KNIGHT WAS OUTLAW ROBINA HOOD IN DISGUISE!
NOW ALAN DALE AND THE SHERIFF COME TO ARREST ME! THERE'S NO ESCAPE!
But —
UNHAND THAT VALIANT MAIDEN, VARLETS!
SEIZE HER IN THE NAME OF THE LAW!
TAKE THAT FOR YOUR LAW!
OOORGH!
AT THEM, FLO! HELP RESCUE ROBINA!
AAAH! OOOH! YAROOOF!
WHAT A FEARFUL AFFRAY! AND ALL ON MY BEHALF!

The Sheriff and his men were soon overpowered.

COME, JANE. LET US AWAY FROM HERE!

WAIT! MY PRINCE WISHES TO REWARD YOU FOR YOUR VALOUR.

BRAVO! NE'ER BEFORE HAVE I SEEN SUCH A MERRY FREE-FOR-ALL! DON DEMONIO REMAINS CHAMPION BUT YOU AND YOUR MAIDS SHALL SHARE THESE PRIZES.

At Christmas Time....

THERE are lots of tales and traditions connected with Christmas, some fact, some fiction, but all fascinating! Here are just a few.

CHRISTMAS cards with messages and bright pictures were first designed about 1843, and as they became more popular there were cards of all shapes and sizes, including crescents, stars, fans and snowballs. Nowadays, millions are sent every year in Britain, and lots of the Victorian type are still selling like hot cakes, particularly skating scenes, snowy landscapes with a stage coach, and Victorian family party scenes. But few people can equal the record of a San Francisco man, Werner Erhard, who posted 62,824 one year! What a lot of stamps!

HOLLY has always been considered a lucky plant, and although the Christmas decorations must be taken down on Twelfth Night, a sprig of holly used to be kept in the belief that it would protect the house from lightning throughout the following year. Holly trees were often planted in gardens as a protection against thunderstorm damage, too.

ROBINS and other birds appreciate a share of the family Christmas dinner, and this is the time of year when they depend on us to feed them! A Victorian Christmas card showing a poor, dead robin in the snow drew attention to the plight of the birds in winter. The things they like best to eat include lumps of suet, bacon rinds, raisins, apple pieces, grapes and strings of peanuts. In cold countries, a sheaf of wheat is sometimes tied to a long pole to provide a feast for the birds, out of the reach of cats. You can make them their own little Christmas pudding, and tie it by string to a tree branch or the washing line. All you need is a small ball of fat or suet rolled in birdseed, and/or grated apple and crumbs.

PART of the Christmas decorations used to be ivy intertwined with holly. An old legend says that if ivy is taken into the house before holly, the women and girls will rule the roost all through the festive season and the year following it. Traditionally the holly represents man and the ivy, woman.

SNOW is part of the Christmas scene on cards, but even if we don't get a white Christmas you can make your own yummy mini snowballs from left-over plum pud. Heat it well, then mould it into small balls and toss each one in icing sugar till it's completely covered. They're scrumptious!

THE Christmas tree we know only came to Britain in Victorian days, when the Queen's husband, Prince Albert, had one for the royal children at Windsor. There's a legend which tells how a woman who lived long ago made such a wonderful job of decorating a tree for her family, spiders rewarded her by weaving webs all over it. These were magically turned to gold and silver, and became the very first tinsel trimmings!

MISTLETOE means "Give me a kiss" in the language of flowers, but for every one exchanged under the mistletoe bough a berry must be removed. The parasitic mistletoe was reckoned to have a special magic in bygone days because it grew fresh and green on leafless trees. Any girl who wanted to attract a boy, pricked his initials on a mistletoe leaf with a pin and tucked the leaf into her bodice, next her skin, as a magical charm.

SANTA CLAUS is short for Saint Nicholas, a kindly bishop who in days of long ago gave three girls the money they needed before they could be married. He threw purses of gold through the open window of their home, and the money fell into their stockings which were hanging by the fire. Ever since, people have been hopefully hanging up their stockings for presents. And in some countries Santa fills childrens' shoes with goodies. Santa's workshop actually exists and is near Lake Placid in America where there are ten log cabins, one of which is Santa's home. His staff stay busy all year making toys, and there is also pasture land where his reindeer graze.

There's also a village in Indiana called Santa Claus and a man who lives in Los Angeles changed his name from Wilfred Holley to the even more Christmassy one of Santa Claus. He suits it, too, as he has a white beard and whiskers, a beaming red face and bright blue eyes — just like the real Santa Claus!

TOP PETS

Each picture wins £3

Rachel and Lyndsey Thomas, Darlington

Allison Smith, Wormit

Joanna Hendry, Falkirk

Carmel Kelly, Dublin

Deborah Furlong, Coventry

Louise Greig, Carnoustie

Bronwen Ellmore, Powys

Christina Chatwin Redditch

MOLLY MASON was the matron at Burleigh School for Boys. Although she was small, she usually managed the pupils better than most of the teachers!

OH, DEAR! IT MUST BE A FREE PERIOD. THE BOYS ARE DOING ALL THE WRONG THINGS!

WE COULD PAY A VISIT TO BARTON HOUSE. IT'S A LOVELY ELIZABETHAN BUILDING NOT FAR FROM HERE, FAMOUS FOR ITS FINE FURNITURE AND PAINTINGS.

WE'RE QUITE HAPPY DOING NOTHING MUCH, MATRON. THANKS ANYWAY.

DOING NOTHING ISN'T GOOD FOR YOU, BOYS. TOMORROW'S SATURDAY. I'LL TAKE YOU OUT FOR THE DAY. BARTON HOUSE HAS SOME OF THE MOST COLOURFUL GARDENS IN THE COUNTRY. WE COULD HAVE A PICNIC THERE!
BUT WE WERE GOING TO WATCH TV, MATRON. THERE'S A FOOTBALL MATCH BETWEEN ENGLAND AND SCOTLAND TOMORROW!

Even the Head wasn't too keen on Molly's idea—
I'D MUCH RATHER THE BOYS STAYED WHERE I COULD KEEP AN EYE ON THEM, MOLLY. THEY MIGHT BE A BIT OF A HANDFUL AT BARTON HOUSE.
BUT I CAN HANDLE THEM, HEADMASTER.

I'VE GOT A DREADFUL HEADACHE COMING ON.
IN THAT CASE, IT WOULD BE BETTER IF I TOOK THE BOYS AWAY AND LEFT YOU IN PEACE, HEADMASTER.

The next morning—
CHICKEN, APPLE PIES, SAUSAGE ROLLS, CHEESE BAPS AND SPICE CAKE. YOU'VE DONE US PROUD, COOK.
BUT HAVE YOU SEEN THE WEATHER, MOLLY? IT'S NOT THE SORT OF DAY FOR A PICNIC.
IT IS RATHER A DULL DAY, BUT IT'S STILL DRY. I THINK WE'LL RISK IT.

Molly retrieved her cushion from Clark's shirt, and —

But shortly afterwards —
HEY, THIS IS GREAT! WHERE DID YOU LEARN TO DRIVE LIKE THIS, MATRON?
MY DAD WAS A FARMER. I USED TO DRIVE THE CATTLE TO MARKET. NOW, WHERE'S MY NAVIGATOR?
IT'S THE NEXT TURNING ON THE LEFT, MATRON. DO THEY HAVE WILD ANIMALS AT BARTON HOUSE?
YES, THEY HAVE. I HOPE YOU BROUGHT YOUR CAMERAS, BOYS.
And in the grounds of Barton House —
HOLD IT, MATRON! THIS WILL MAKE A GREAT PICTURE FOR MY ALBUM.
I THINK THE BOYS ARE GOING TO ENJOY THEMSELVES AFTER ALL.
STUPID THINGS! THEY'VE ALL RUN OFF. WE DIDN'T DO ANYTHING TO FRIGHTEN THEM.
I HOPE YOU MANAGED TO GET YOUR PICTURE, JIM.
Suddenly the heavens opened —
DRAT! IT'S A CLOUDBURST! RUN FOR IT!
THOSE GIRAFFES WEREN'T SO SILLY AFTER ALL. THEY KNEW THE RAIN WAS COMING.
IT'S NICE AND WARM INSIDE, BOYS. WE'LL BE ABLE TO SEE THE MAGNIFICENT STATE ROOMS AND FINE FURNITURE.
HUH! IMAGINE GETTING SOAKED AND BORED ALL IN ONE DAY!

ISN'T THIS LOVELY, BOYS? SOME OF THIS FURNITURE MUST BE WORTH A FORTUNE.
THIS MAGNIFICENT BED IS CARVED WITH THE LETTERS J.R. IT IS BELIEVED TO HAVE BELONGED TO JAMES THE SECOND.
MAYBE IT CAME FROM DALLAS. HO, HO!
J.R.
THIS IS ABSOLUTELY OUTRAGEOUS!
GOODNESS! WHAT'S HAPPENED?
IT'S BILLY!
NNNNNNN
JUST TYPICAL OF THE YOUTH OF TODAY!
J.R.
I HEARD HE WAS A BURLEIGH BOY. THEY SHOULD BE BANNED FROM VISITING STATELY HOMES!
I DO ASSURE YOU THAT BURLEIGH BOYS ARE NORMALLY WELL-BEHAVED, MADAM!
I'D BETTER ROUND UP THE BOYS. OH, DEAR! THREE SEEM TO BE MISSING!

WHEN ARE WE GOING TO HAVE OUR FOOD, MATRON? I'M FADING AWAY TO NOTHING.
WE CAN'T EAT UNTIL WE'RE ALL TOGETHER, BILLY. HELP ME FIND THE OTHERS.
JIM, TOBY AND TOWERS WENT UP THERE ABOUT TEN MINUTES AGO, MATRON.
OH, NO! I'LL HAVE TO SNEAK UP AND FIND THEM.
PRIVATE KEEP OUT
LOOK AT THAT! ONE OF THOSE DREADFUL PUPILS IS SNEAKING INTO THE PRIVATE QUARTERS!
SHE'S NO PUPIL — SHE'S OUR MATRON — AND WE DON'T LIKE ANYONE CALLING HER NAMES!
THESE PAINTINGS LOOK REALLY VALUABLE. I DO HOPE THE BOYS HAVEN'T TOUCHED THEM!
BOYS! THANK GOODNESS I'VE FOUND YOU!
SSH! WE'RE TRACKING DOWN A CROOK, MATRON!
WE CREPT UP HERE TO HAVE A LOOK, MATRON, THEN WE SAW THIS BURGLAR PINCH A PICTURE.

Moments later, the thief — and the painting — were in custody.

THESE ARE QUITE THE MOST DELICIOUS CAKES I'VE EVER TASTED, SIR.
AH, YES, MY COOK BAKES THEM SPECIALLY FOR MY DISTINGUISHED GUESTS. I FIND THEM HARD TO RESIST MYSELF.
I ALSO HAVE ANOTHER WEAKNESS, BOYS — THAT'S WATCHING SOCCER. ENGLAND AND SCOTLAND ARE PLAYING TODAY.
BUT IT WILL ALL BE OVER BY NOW, SIR.
But the Marquis had made a video recording —
GOAL!
NO, IT'S NOT! WHAT A SAVE!
THIS DAY WILL GO DOWN IN HISTORY AT BURLEIGH SCHOOL. I CAN'T WAIT TO SEE THE HEAD'S FACE WHEN I SHOW HIM THIS PICTURE!

TOOTS
I'D LOVE TO HAVE A DONKEY RIDE ON THE BEACH.
DONKEY RIDES
RIGHT, TOOTS. YOU CAN HAVE BILLY. JUMP ON.
COME ON, BILLY. GEE UP!
I'M NOT MOVING! I'VE HAD ENOUGH FOR ONE DAY!
"I'VE CARRIED FAT RIDERS —"
"WOULD-BE JOCKEYS —"
"NOT TO MENTION THE COWBOYS!"
SORRY, TOOTS. HAVE YOUR MONEY BACK. BILLY MUST BE NEEDING A REST!
HUH! I WAS REALLY LOOKING FORWARD TO A RIDE.
BEACH ZOO
WAIT A MINUTE! I KNOW—
—AND IT WOULD BE A GREAT ADVERT FOR THE ZOO.
ZOO
YES, WHY NOT?
ZOO
THIS IS THE LIFE!
THIS IS MORE LIKE IT! AND CHARLIE THE CAMEL FEELS RIGHT AT HOME ON THE BEACH!
VISIT the BEACH ZOO

Willa the Wisp

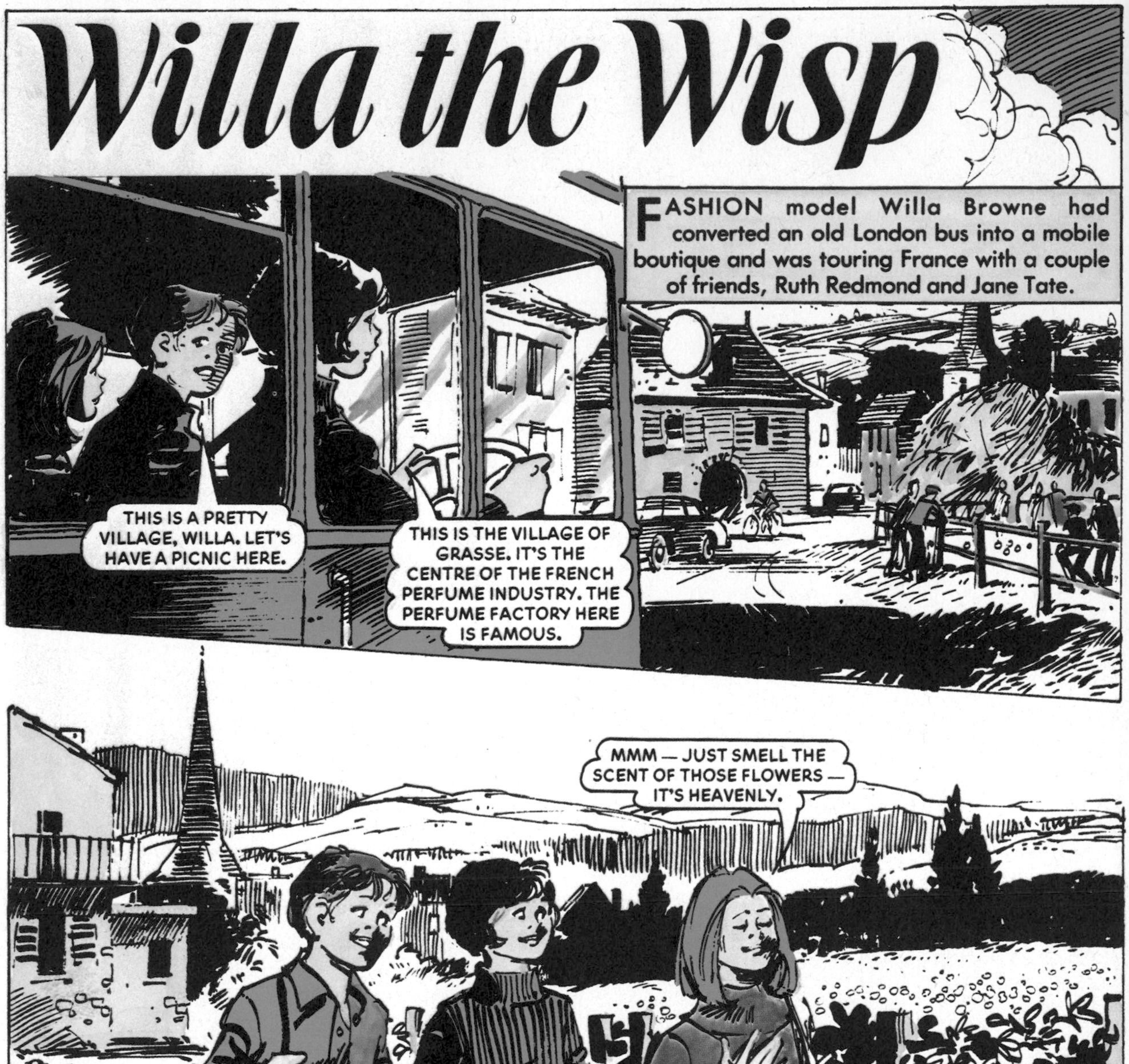

FASHION model Willa Browne had converted an old London bus into a mobile boutique and was touring France with a couple of friends, Ruth Redmond and Jane Tate.

THIS IS A PRETTY VILLAGE, WILLA. LET'S HAVE A PICNIC HERE.

THIS IS THE VILLAGE OF GRASSE. IT'S THE CENTRE OF THE FRENCH PERFUME INDUSTRY. THE PERFUME FACTORY HERE IS FAMOUS.

MMM — JUST SMELL THE SCENT OF THOSE FLOWERS — IT'S HEAVENLY.

A STRAW HAT FOR YOU AND YOU — AND ONE FOR ME! WE'RE FLOWER-PICKERS FOR THE DAY.

WE NEED SOME READY CASH, GIRLS. BUSINESS HASN'T BEEN TOO GOOD LATELY.
WELL, YOU CAN GIVE ME WORK LIKE THIS ANY TIME! IT'S LOVELY TO BE IN THE OPEN AIR!

THE OLD BUS IS NEEDING SOME NEW TYRES. WE'VE COVERED SOME MILES ON THIS TOUR, GIRLS. WHAT'S THAT NOISE?
SOB SOB... SOB
SOUNDS LIKE SOMEONE CRYING.

IT CAME FROM OVER THERE. LET'S TAKE A LOOK!

HELLO, THERE. IS SOMETHING WRONG?
I HAVE BEEN ROBBED!
WAIT A MOMENT! PERHAPS WE CAN HELP.

OH, DEAR! NOW SHE'S FALLEN. COME ON, LET'S SEE IF SHE'S O.K.
IT'S MY LEG — I CAN'T PUT MY WEIGHT ON IT.
I THINK SHE'LL NEED A DOCTOR.
I'LL STAY WITH HER WHILE YOU FETCH HELP.
I DON'T THINK ANYTHING IS BROKEN. IT'S PROBABLY A BAD SPRAIN.
COULD YOU GET ME A DRINK OF WATER, PLEASE?
JANE! DON'T LEAVE THE GIRL ALONE. WE'RE GOING TO GET THE DOCTOR. WE GOT THE ADDRESS FROM THE FOREMAN.
SHE JUST WANTED A GLASS OF WATER. I THINK SHE'S FEELING FAINT.
I HOPE SHE HASN'T FAINTED. OH, NO! SHE'S GONE!

Meanwhile—
THE DOCTOR LIVES SOMEWHERE ALONG THIS ROAD —
WILLA, YOU'RE ALMOST OUT OF PETROL.
BUS BOUTIQUE
THERE'S THE DOCTOR'S HOUSE. I'LL GET SOME PETROL AT THAT FILLING STATION WHILE YOU FETCH THE DOCTOR, RUTH.

THAT'S STRANGE. I CAN'T FIND MY PURSE!

RUTH, CAN YOU LEND ME SOME MONEY? I DON'T SEEM TO HAVE MY PURSE WITH ME.
OF COURSE, WILLA.
BOUTIQUE

But—
OH, NO! MY PURSE ISN'T HERE!
The doctor drove Willa and Ruth back—
I HAD TO LEAVE MY WATCH AT THE GARAGE AS SECURITY FOR THE PETROL. LET'S HOPE JANE HAS SOME CASH LEFT — AND THAT WE FIND OUR PURSES!

After a week, the girls had made friends with the other flower pickers.

YES, IT IS LOVELY, BUT NOT FOR LONG. SCIENCE HAS FOUND CHEAPER WAYS OF MAKING PERFUME WITHOUT FLOWERS. SOON THERE WILL BE NO WORK HERE.
OH, DEAR. THAT'S VERY SAD.

That evening—
IT'S OUR TURN TO PROVIDE THE ENTERTAINMENT TONIGHT, GIRLS. SO A FASHION SHOW IS WHAT WE DO BEST!
I DON'T THINK IT WILL HELP US MUCH, THOUGH. THE FLOWER PICKERS ARE QUITE POOR.

GOOD EVENING, EVERYONE. WELCOME TO OUR FASHION SHOW. FIRST OF ALL, HERE'S RUTH WEARING A LONG SKIRT WITH A FRESH, CHECKED SHIRT—

NOW, HERE IS JANE WEARING THE POPULAR SLIT SKIRT—
GOODNESS! THERE'S THE GIRL WHO ROBBED US!

Jane took over from Willa—
GOT YOU! I HOPE I'VE CAUGHT YOU BEFORE YOU ROBBED SOMEONE ELSE!
OH, PLEASE LET ME GO! I—I AM NOT A THIEF!

I HAVE NEVER STOLEN ANYTHING BEFORE. I CAME BACK TO RETURN THESE.
WHAT MADE YOU STEAL OUR PURSES, THEN?

The girl took Willa, Ruth and Jane to see her mother.
MY MOTHER IS VERY FRAIL. I PICKED FLOWERS TO PAY THE DOCTOR'S BILLS, BUT SOON THE PERFUME FACTORY WILL CLOSE AND THERE WILL BE NO MORE WORK. I STOLE YOUR PURSES, BUT I WAS SO ASHAMED —

WHERE DID YOU GET THESE LOVELY GLOVES?
MAMA MADE THESE PERFUMED GLOVES SOME YEARS AGO.
PERFUMED GLOVES? WHAT A SUPER IDEA!

Willa asked the girl's mother how the gloves were made. Then, later—
MY BACK IS STILL ACHING FROM THE FLOWER PICKING. NOW I'M BENT OVER A SEWING MACHINE!
BUT IF THIS PLAN WORKS, WE'LL LINE EVERYONE'S POCKETS, JANE!

A few days later, in Paris—
HANK, LOOK AT THIS! ONLY PARIS COULD HAVE SUCH A DARLING IDEA! WE MUST BUY LOTS TO TAKE HOME!
GOOD OLD WILLA! SHE'S REVIVED AN OLD CUSTOM AND IT LOOKS LIKE THE PERFUME FACTORY IS SAVED! WHAT WILL SHE THINK OF NEXT?
BUS BOUTIQ
SILK PERFUME GLOVES STRAIGHT FROM GRASSE GUARANTEED TO COOL THE HOTTEST HAN

IT'S PAULA!

Hi, girls!

I was delighted when the Ed asked me to fill nine pages of this year's annual, so I've prepared a wide range of features which I hope you'll enjoy. First of all, though, here's the type of page I put together regularly for the weekly "Bunty".

'Bye,

Paula

BEAUTY SPOT

NAIL CARE

The Festive Season — and especially Christmas — is a time for looking your best. But it's also a very hectic period when you may not have as much time as you'd like to look after your nails. So here are a few hints to help you keep them in trim.

1. Gently remove all polish using a good conditioning remover.
2. Use the pale side of an emery board to shape nails — holding board at a slight angle so nails are filed from underneath. Stroke from each side of the nail towards the centre, creating a soft oval shape.
3. Apply a small amount of cuticle remover to help eliminate unwanted cuticle. Carefully push the cuticle back with a cotton wool-wrapped orange stick, then wash off all excess with warm water.
4. Apply some nail treatment cream to replace essential moisture. This helps prevent flaking or peeling.
5. 'Hard as Nails' clear nail protector from Sally Hansen will make a perfect base coat and will enable you to wear your favourite colour as often as you wish without the problem of discolouration.
6. Apply two coats of your favourite colour. Then, finally, apply a coat of 'Super Shine' also from Sally Hansen, to give a glossy finish and a longer life to your polish.

Once you've got your nails in shape, it will be easier to make a New Year resolution to keep them that way!

CROSSWORD

CLUES — ACROSS

1. Guidance (9)
5. Wound with a dagger (4)
7. Turn in a road (4)
8. Kingdom (5)
10. Piece of wood (5)
13. Sailor's greeting (4)
14. Retain (4)
15. Autumn month (9)

CLUES — DOWN

1. Powdery matter (4)
2. At the back (4)
3. Article (4)
4. Unclothed figure (4)
6. Stomach (5)
7. Eyelid movement (5)
9. Low part in music (4)
10. High deck (4)
11. Pavement edge (4)
12. Box (4)

SOLUTIONS

ACROSS: 1. Direction **5.** Stab **7.** Bend **8.** Realm **10.** Plank **13.** Ahoy **14.** Keep **15.** September
DOWN: 1. Dust **2.** Rear **3.** Item **4.** Nude **6.** Belly **7.** Blink **9.** Bass **10.** Poop **11.** Kerb **12.** Spar

I'M A FITNESS FAN

Keeping fit is something that's very important. An evening a week dancing at the local disco helps me keep in trim, but I also go jogging, and I cycle to and from work.

Jogging, cycling, and also swimming are excellent and reasonably inexpensive ways to keep fit.

I jog in the park. I hate running on roads. Remember, though, if you're thinking of starting, to begin with only five or ten minutes, building up the duration of your run as you feel more capable. This way you'll strengthen your leg muscles and build stamina at the same time.

Cycling keeps the muscles of the legs and waist nicely toned up. And it's a very pleasant way to get to and from school.

Finally, swimming is an excellent all-round exercise for the whole body. And you will be learning a discipline which could save your life!

COOK'S CORNER

Here's a recipe for a super sweet to titillate your tastebuds, perhaps on Boxing Day, after all the heavy turkey and Christmas pud of the day before.

APRICOT DELIGHT

Ingredients

8 oz. (200 grams) dried apricots
2 teaspoons powdered gelatine
2 tablespoons water
1 small can Nestle Tip Top
1 teaspoon lemon juice
Lemon slices for decoration.

Method

Place the apricots in a large bowl. Add sufficient water to cover and leave overnight. Dissolve the gelatine in the water in a small bowl held over a saucepan of hot water. Place the apricots, their liquid made up to ¾ pint with water, gelatine and Tip Top in a blender or food processor. Blend until smooth, and stir in the lemon juice. Spoon into 6 individual glasses and decorate with twists of lemon.

WARNING! Ask an adult's permission before using a hot cooker.

SAFARI GAME
To set the ball — or dice — rolling, I've worked out a game with one of the lovely cartoonists in our art department. I got the idea when I visited a Safari Park during the summer.
HOW TO PLAY
We're off on safari, girls, and any number can take part! All you need is a dice, and a button or coin for each player. You must throw a six to start, then off you go, following the instructions. First home to the village is the winner, and you must throw the exact number to finish.
START
1
2
3 TIED UP WITH NEW FRIEND. MISS A TURN.
4
5
6 HITCH A LIFT ON ZEBRA. ON TO 11.
7
8
9
10
11
12 SHORT CUT UP THE GIRAFFE'S NECK. ON TO 15.
13
14
15
16
17
18
19 STOP TO READ "IT'S PAULA" IN "BUNTY". MISS A TURN.
20
BUNTY
35
36
37 HAVE A REST. MISS A TURN.
38
39 ATTACKED BY MONKEYS. BACK TO 36.
Safari so good!

25
24
26
23 SPOTTED BY A LEOPARD! MISS A TURN.
27 SWING ACROSS TO 50!
Whee!
Nice pussy!
22
28
29
30
31
32 GORILLA TROUBLE! BACK TO 26.
33
Go on! Give me a cuddle!
Get lost!
51
50
52 DODGE THAT RHINO. MISS A TURN.
53
49 SHORT CUT TO 54.
48
54
55
47
46
56 WATCH THAT POOL! TOO LATE! MISS A TURN TO DRY OFF.
57
45
58
44
59 NEARLY THERE! THROW A ONE TO FINISH!
SPLOOSH!
43
42 STOP FOR A BATH. MISS A TURN.
41
Glub!
Yippee! I'm home!

CAROLYN OF

ONE OF MY ALL-TIME FAVOURITE CAREER IDEAS WAS TO JOIN A CIRCUS. WORKING WITH ANIMALS — THE THRILL OF THE BIG TOP — THE CONSTANT ACTIVITY AND EXCITEMENT WHILE GETTING THE SHOW READY EVERY NIGHT — IT ALL SEEMED SO ATTRACTIVE. BUT CIRCUS LIFE ISN'T FUN, FUN, FUN ALL THE WAY, AS YOU'LL FIND OUT IN THIS SUPER INTERVIEW. IT'S SELDOM DULL, THOUGH!

Parade of the Smurfs!

CAROLYN ROBERTS is only eleven, but already she is a star of the sawdust ring in the family circus.

Her mum is a trapeze artiste, and also stars in an act where she balances on a great silver globe as it rolls along, and in another act with horses. In a spectacular called 'Star Wars', she performs acrobatics on a big, crescent moon, high in the Big Top.

Carolyn's dad is one of the world famous Roberts family, and has done just about every sort of act in the ring, from clowning and boxing a kangaroo to presenting elephants, leopards and lions.

Just like Mum! Carolyn learns the globe balancing act.

"My Dad didn't intend to be a lion tamer," Carolyn explained. "He had to take over one night when the man who'd been in the lion act for twenty years decided to quit!"

Carolyn herself first appeared in the ring at the age of five! This is quite usual for children brought up to circus life. Their parents take them into the ring to 'take a call' which means stepping gracefully forward with hands raised as the audience applauds during the parade of artistes which closes the show.

"Right now I have an act with my pony, Prince," Carolyn said, "and also on the globe. I take part in our presentation of the Smurfs, along with other circus children including my brother, Johnboy, who is nine. My little sister, Janna, is only three, so she hasn't been in anything yet and has to stay at home in the caravan during the performance."

Carolyn is also planning to have a dog act showing four Samoyeds, three poodles, and one Jack Russell terrier in lots of tricks.

"I'm getting the poodles from Sally Chipperfield," she told me. Sally belongs to the Chipperfield circus.

But life isn't all sawdust and animals for Carolyn. She has a busy life outside the ring, and attends the Roberts Mobile Circus School every day along with a dozen or so classmates, including Johnboy.

The parents of all these children are on tour with the circus, and their headmaster is Mr Haslet, whose son, Daniel, and daughter, Naomi, are in the school. He takes his pupils on an educational visit to a museum or castle every week, and they see a great deal of Britain and learn loads of history and geography that way.

He also plays the guitar, for singing lessons. So nobody ever wants to skip *this* school!

Sometimes the circus stays at the same site for ten days, but more often packing and unpacking, settling the animals in new quarters, and putting up and taking down the Big Top are jobs which must be done every third day. This means a lot of work for the adults, but for Carolyn and her friends lessons continue just as usual, and all the pupils in the school are well advanced for their ages.

"The girls seem to be cleverer than the boys though," Mr Haslet admits. "About two years ahead of them in school work, I'd say!"

As well as her rehearsing and time in the classroom,

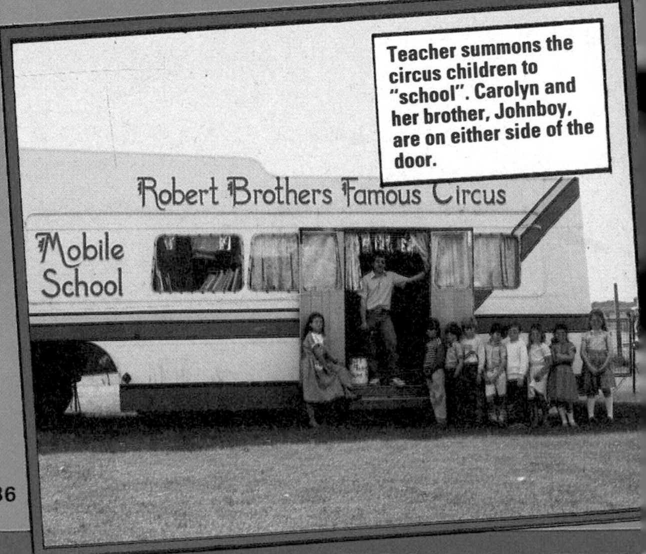

Teacher summons the circus children to "school". Carolyn and her brother, Johnboy, are on either side of the door.

THE CIRCUS

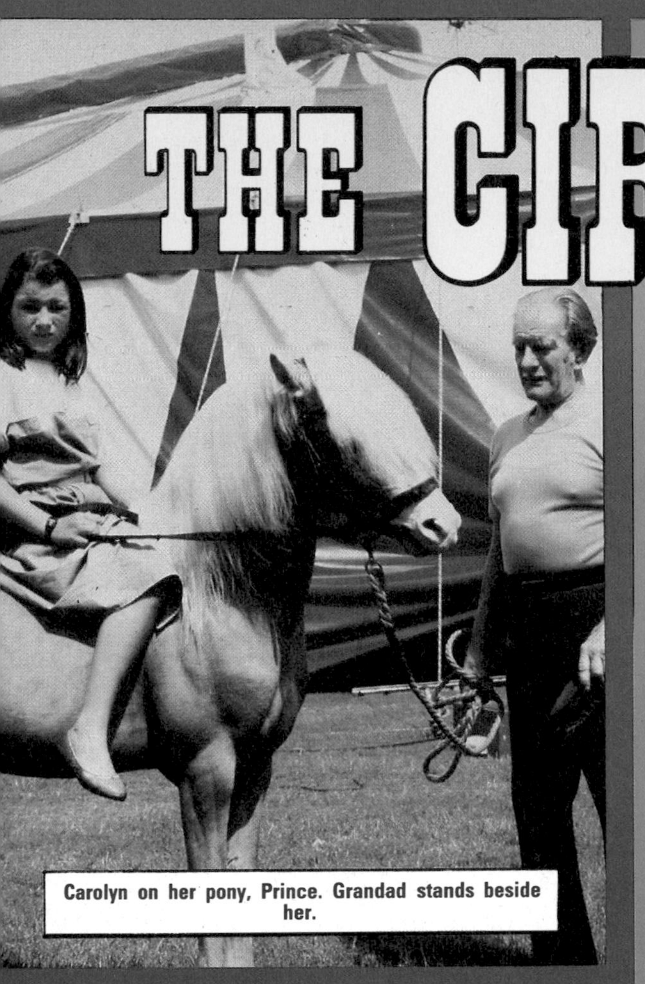
Carolyn on her pony, Prince. Grandad stands beside her.

Alsatians, are a bit scared of Dallas and J.R."

The circus is on tour for ten months of the year, and Carolyn would hate to live in a house.

"It would make me sick," she said firmly. "We do have a farm, and I don't mind staying there for a couple of months in winter, especially around Christmas. The only thing I hate about going back on the road to tour is leaving my friend, Melissa, who stays near the farm. But I have lots of friends here too."

As she spoke, Carolyn put an arm round Emma whose dad is the circus signwriter.

Carolyn hasn't yet decided what she wants to be when she leaves school. But she'll certainly be staying with the circus and trying lots of different acts.

"Johnboy loves the elephants best," she said, "but I have no special favourites. I just know it's all going to be a lot of fun."

So far as Carolyn Roberts is concerned, there's quite definitely no business like show business — and the magical world of the circus ring!

Hard at work in their mobile school.

Carolyn must help with household chores. When I first met her she was going shopping to a supermarket near the circus site.

She sees a great deal of her parents and grandparents, who also travel with the circus, and her grandad, Tommy Roberts, can often be persuaded to groom her pony for her. It's also Grandad who packs and unpacks the beautiful collection of fine china and glass animals and clowns in her gran and grandad's big family caravan which has five rooms!

It was Carolyn's grandad who taught her to ride, and her mum was her teacher at balancing on the globes; Mum belongs to a famous Italian circus family.

Carolyn (front row) holds Janna, Mum holds J.R., Gran, Grandad, Johnboy and Dad are all in the background.

Amongst the animals in the Roberts family at present are four lions, four elephants, two camels, a goat, a donkey and twelve beautiful horses and ponies.

"When my dad was little he had lion cubs as playmates, and used to bath them in the caravan by the heat of the stove," Carolyn said. "My grandparents even let leopard cubs into the 'van living room to romp about, and their favourite toy was a hearth brush. But now Gran and Grandad just have two chihuahua dogs called J.R. and Dallas. They may be tiny, but they're good watch dogs. In fact the circus guard dogs,

Carolyn and Johnboy on the steps of their beautiful caravan home.

BE A "BUNTY" Supergirl

One of the most popular features of my pages in the weekly "Bunty" is the SUPERGIRL slot. If you would like to be a Supergirl — and win a fiver if your photo's selected for publication — see the weekly "Bunty" for further details. Every picture printed here wins £5.

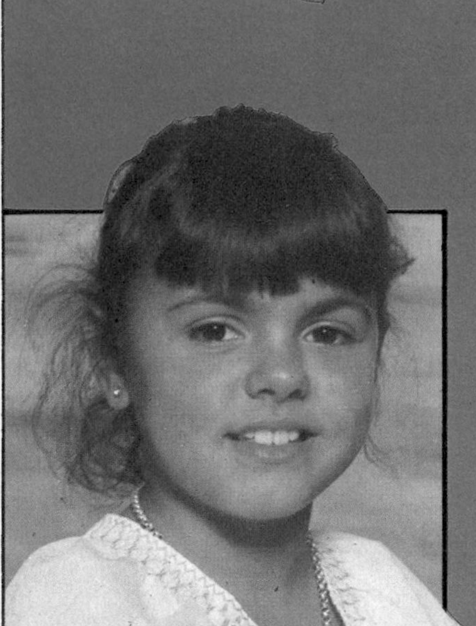

NAME: Sobera Miah
AGE: 10
HOBBIES: Collecting cuddly toys, "Bunty", swimming
FAVOURITE GROUP: Wham!
FAVOURITE PERSONALITY: Bobby Ball
FAVOURITE FOOD: Beefburgers and onions
AMBITION: To meet Bobby Ball

NAME: Julie Owen
AGE: 8
HOBBIES: Music, gym, reading
FAVOURITE GROUP: Duran Duran
FAVOURITE PERSONALITY: Mollie Sugden
FAVOURITE FOOD: Fish fingers
AMBITION: To teach music

NAME: Hazel White
AGE: 5
HOBBIES: Reading "Bunty", roller-skating
FAVOURITE GROUP: Spandau Ballet
FAVOURITE PERSONALITY: Howard Jones
FAVOURITE FOOD: Chicken and chips
AMBITION: To go to America

NAME: Rosemary Farrell
AGE: 11
HOBBIES: Swimming, windsurfing
FAVOURITE GROUP: Wham!
FAVOURITE PERSONALITY: Prince
FAVOURITE FOOD: Chips
AMBITION: To write a comic

NAME: Elizabeth Darby
AGE: 8
HOBBIES: Swimming, reading
FAVOURITE GROUP: Wham!
FAVOURITE PERSONALITY: Orw
FAVOURITE FOOD: Bacon and e
AMBITION: To be a teacher

NAME: Julie Kitchener
AGE: 12
HOBBIES: Hockey, tennis, cricket
FAVOURITE GROUP: Spandau Ballet
FAVOURITE PERSONALITY: Paul Young
FAVOURITE FOOD: Salads and fruit
AMBITION: To be a physiotherapist

NAME: Kelly Andrews
AGE: 11
HOBBIES: Horse riding, swimming, reading "Bunty"
FAVOURITE GROUP: Spandau Ballet
FAVOURITE PERSONALITY: Jan Francis
FAVOURITE FOOD: Spaghetti bolognaise
AMBITION: To be a showjumper

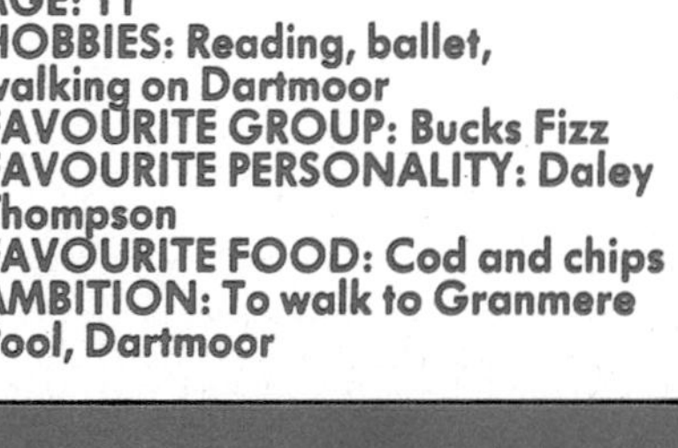

NAME: Claire Cooper
AGE: 11
HOBBIES: Reading, ballet, walking on Dartmoor
FAVOURITE GROUP: Bucks Fizz
FAVOURITE PERSONALITY: Daley Thompson
FAVOURITE FOOD: Cod and chips
AMBITION: To walk to Granmere Pool, Dartmoor

NAME: Amie Chaplin
AGE: 8
HOBBIES: Reading, drawing, horse-riding
FAVOURITE GROUP: Wham!
FAVOURITE PERSONALITY: Paul Young
FAVOURITE FOOD: Chips
AMBITION: To own a horse-riding school

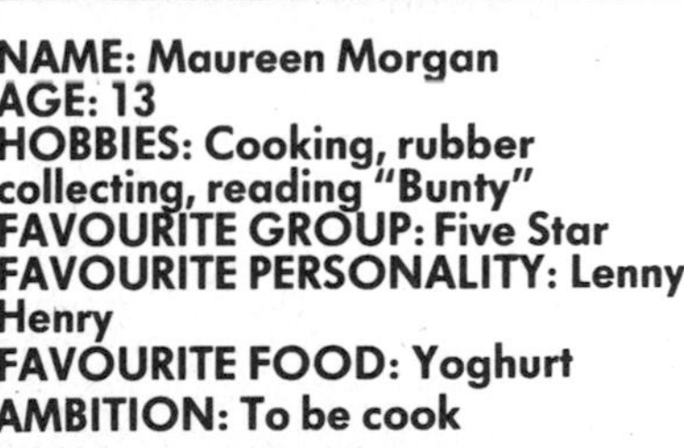

NAME: Maureen Morgan
AGE: 13
HOBBIES: Cooking, rubber collecting, reading "Bunty"
FAVOURITE GROUP: Five Star
FAVOURITE PERSONALITY: Lenny Henry
FAVOURITE FOOD: Yoghurt
AMBITION: To be cook

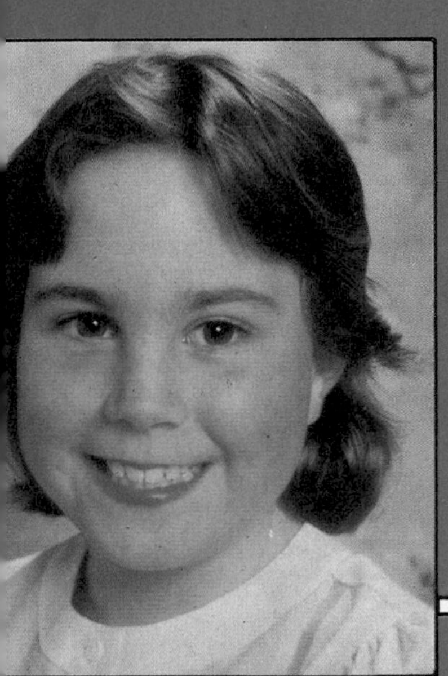

NAME: Jean Davies
AGE: 10
HOBBIES: Running, gymnastics, badminton, netball
FAVOURITE GROUP: Prince and the Revolution
FAVOURITE PERSONALITY: Prince
FAVOURITE FOOD: Chow mein
AMBITION: To be an athlete

Here's a wonderful potted history of dolls I just know you'll enjoy. Dolls which speak, open and close their eyes, and wet their nappies aren't as ultra-modern as you might have thought!

THE history of dolls is as old as time, but the oldest British doll still in existence dates from the reign of Henry VIII. She's made of wood with a plaster face and a red velvet dress, and not surprisingly looks a bit tatty by now even though she's in a museum.

Early dolls were usually of wood, or made of cloth and called rag dolls. But in Victorian times wax was used, which gave a very lifelike effect, but melted if dolly was left lying in the sun or too near a hot fire. Wax could also crack, so a doll like this was a very precious plaything often kept for Sundays.

During the week, wooden dolls with painted faces and moveable arms were popular and made in all sizes. There were big ones, and also the penny size sold by Swiss girls in the streets of British cities who attracted customers with their cry of 'Buy a doll, buy a doll, from sweet Rose of Lucerne'. Although very cheap, they were beautifully carved and no two were exactly the same.

The lovely big doll wearing the white dress trimmed with pink ribbons is Rebecca, who is made of wax and has real hair. Just look at her beautiful little hands and sweet face.

REBECCA — wax doll.

Doll manufacturers bought hair from wigmakers, and when brushed and combed it had a silken sheen. So dolly's tresses were given a hundred long, sweeping strokes of the brush every night, like those of her young owner.

The other big doll, Genevra, is made of china and really dressed in the height of Edwardian style! She's wearing six petticoats!

GENEVRA — china Edwardian doll.

Genevra was made in Germany over eighty years ago, and, like Rebecca, is big enough to wear baby clothes. But girls of the past often made dresses and undies for their dolls. Queen Victoria sewed for twenty of her doll family, and Louisa May Alcott, who wrote 'Little Women', one of the best-selling books of all time, earned pocket money as a dolls' dressmaker when she was a schoolgirl. All her classmates bought from her.

Another thing girls liked to do was make gorgeous screens covered thickly with scraps, and Rebecca and Genevra are pictured standing against a background of one of those Victorian screens.

Sleeping dolls which open and shut their eyes are not so modern as you might think. The first ones were made in 1826. And so were talking dolls which said 'Mama' and 'Papa'.

Paper dolls made from thick cardboard are no new thing either, as the first doll dressing books date from around 1700!

When Hans Christian Andersen told his famous fairytales he illustrated them by cutting out paper dolls, castles, swans etc. Some women's magazines had cut-out doll pages and a popular American one featured a baby doll and its clothes. This was called 'Kewpie Kutouts'.

Those cute Kewpie dolls became part of the fun of the fair where they were given as sideshow prizes, and most of them were small. But the one in our picture is an outsize Kewpie named Katy, wearing white tights, red dress, and black patent shoes which would fit a three-year-old. She looks a real pal, doesn't she? The kind to tell secrets to and watch TV with. She's also a lot of fun to bath and dress, and won't break.

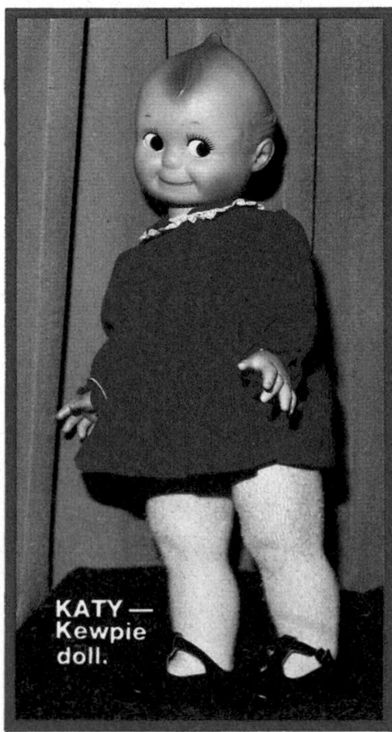

KATY — Kewpie doll.

Unbreakable dolls were only invented about fifty years ago, and between them and wax dolls came china headed ones. They were really beautiful, and if their heads broke

Dolls THROUGH THE AGES

they could be replaced at dolls' hospitals. Every big city had such a hospital and what a thrill it was for any schoolgirl who came home to find her broken baby doll sitting up on her bed as good as new, chubby arms stretched out in welcome.

In 1930, the Dy-Dee doll was invented which could drink from a feeding bottle and wet its nappy. This baby doll was patronised by Royalty when the Duchess of Kent bought one for her daughter.

Much more recently Tiny Tears has been a best selling doll and also the Cabbage Patch Kids.

MYRNA MAY - plush baby doll.

But the plush, cuddly doll in this picture is Myrna May who was made many years before Cabbage Patch Kids hit the headlines. Inside the label on Myrna May's arm there is a message for whoever adopts her which reads as follows:—

'Myrna May is a new born baby. She is very special and needs a very good home. Please make sure she is changed often and given a lot of care'.

Amongst the most popular doll dressing books of this century were Shirley Temple ones with a cardboard figure of the child film star and paper versions of her fabulous clothes. This was in the 1930s and most schoolgirls had chocolate boxes full of Shirley Temple dresses, coats, nightwear, beachwear and playsuits.

SHIRLEY TEMPLE— character doll.

There were also unbreakable Shirley Temple dolls like the one shown in the picture. Extra clothes could be bought for her of the type you get for Sindy and Barbie today, but not so trendy, as Shirley wasn't a teenage style doll.

Dolls modelled on real people were called 'character dolls' and there was a Princess Elizabeth one (the little princess is now the Queen)

EDWARDIAN SAILOR DOLLS.

a Christopher Robin doll, and a range of beautiful brown plush dolls designed by Norah Wellings. They included South Sea Islanders in grass skirts, Girl Guides, golfers and many more. Her souvenir sailor dolls were sold on Cunard liners as souvenirs of Mediterranean cruises which only rich people could afford.

But the ones in our picture are Edwardian sailors and date from the time when many boys and girls wore a navy or red sailor suit for Saturday and a white one for Sunday!

The very latest in character dolls is the Princess Diana one. Bride dolls have always been popular but this one will probably change hands as a valuable antique in time to come.

PRINCESS DIANA— bride doll.

Only twenty-five of these dolls were made and the wedding dress is of the most pure and delicate silk. Both it and the veil are exact copies of the real thing, and so is the tiny bouquet.

This doll is destined to be kept in a glass case, and admired from a distance like the smart fashion dolls of the past.

But most dolls are just made to be loved, and often come to be regarded as lifelong friends by their owners, who wouldn't part with a favourite doll for a king's ransom.

Hope you have one you love like that!

Margie's Magic Aunt

But, before Carla could change back—
EEK! WE'RE BEING INVADED! I'D BETTER CALL THE POLICE!

By the time Margie arrived home from school, the fire was out and her aunt was her old self again—
I TELL YOU THE GARDEN SHED WAS BLAZING, AND THERE WAS A FIERCE-LOOKING VIKING CHEERING AS IT BURNED!
POLICE
WHAT AN IMAGINATION YOUR NEIGHBOUR HAS, SISTER DEAR.
OH, DEAR! LOOKS LIKE AUNT CARLA'S BEEN UP TO HER TRICKS AGAIN. AND I DID SO WANT MUM IN A GOOD MOOD TO ASK HER ABOUT THE SCHOOL CAMPING HOLIDAY.

Later—
SCHOOL CAMP? YES! YOU CAN GO, MARGIE, BUT ONLY IF YOU TAKE YOUR CRAZY AUNT WITH YOU.
BUT, MUM, I CAN'T TAKE AUNT CARLA WITH ME. IT WOULDN'T BE ALLOWED!

UNLESS AUNT CARLA GOES WITH YOU, YOU DON'T GO!
OH, AUNT CARLA! WHY CAN'T YOU BEHAVE? I DID SO WANT TO GO TO CAMP, BUT NOW IT'S IMPOSSIBLE.
IT'S A PROBLEM, DEAR — BUT NOT IMPOSSIBLE, SURELY—

WOULDN'T THEY ALLOW YOU TO TAKE A PET?
A PET? I-I DON'T KNOW. BUT WHY? WHAT HAVE YOU IN MIND, AUNT CARLA?

Carla seized her chance to practise for her test—
SUPPOSE I CHANGED INTO A MONKEY—
OR A PARROT!
OUCH! MY EAR!
WHAT ABOUT A PET SNAKE?
EEEK!

MAYBE A DOG WOULD BE BEST. NO ONE COULD OBJECT TO A PET DOG, SURELY?
PHEW! O.K, I'LL SEE WHAT THE TEACHER SAYS.
And so—
THE TEACHER DIDN'T SEEM TOO HAPPY, DEAR. FANCY ASKING IF I WAS HOUSE-TRAINED! I'D A GOOD MIND TO SNAP AT HER ANKLE!
OH, AUNT CARLA, YOU MUST STOP TALKING! I COULD NEVER EXPLAIN A TALKING DOG!
When they arrived at their usual camp-site—
WHAT DO YOU MEAN WE CAN'T USE THE FIELD? FARMER BROWN ENJOYED HAVING —
FARMER BROWN DOESN'T OWN THE FARM NOW — I DO! AND I DON'T WANT A LOAD OF BADLY-BEHAVED BRATS RUNNING WILD OVER IT!
BUT YOU'RE WELCOME TO CAMP IN BUTTERCUP DELL — ABOUT HALF A MILE IN THAT DIRECTION.
WELL, I SUPPOSE THAT'S SOMETHING.
BUTTERCUP DELL SOUNDS RATHER NICE—
But it was very far from nice!
OH, NO! IT'S A DUMP! LOOK!
WE HAVE NO CHOICE, CHILDREN. WE'LL HAVE TO CLEAR IT UP A BIT, AND GET THE TENTS ERECTED.
THE STREAM'S DRIED UP! WHERE WILL WE GET FRESH WATER?
I'LL JUST TROT OFF FOR A WHILE, MARGIE. I'LL SNIFF OUT SOME FRESH WATER FOR YOU ALL, AND A LITTLE MAGIC MIGHTN'T GO AMISS.
O.K, AUNT. BUT DO BE CAREFUL!
So, out of sight of the camp—
HECKATEY, PECKATEY, MOTHER AND DAUGHTER, FILL THE BED WITH FRESH, CLEAR WATER—

And—
HEY! THE STREAM'S FILLING UP! AND WE'VE EVEN GOT A WATERFALL!
THAT'S A STROKE OF GOOD LUCK! IT WON'T BE SO BAD HERE AFTER ALL!
WELL DONE, AUNT! MAYBE BRINGING YOU ALONG WASN'T SUCH A BAD IDEA!
But the farmer wasn't so happy!
THEY'RE STILL HERE! BUT I'LL FIX 'EM — I'LL DRIVE MY COWS IN AMONG THEIR TENTS TONIGHT.

And so, after dark—
I CAN HEAR COWS! WHAT'S HAPPENING? HELP!

In Margie's tent—
WHAT'S GOING ON, DEAR?
WE'VE BEEN INVADED BY COWS! YOU'D BETTER DO SOMETHING, AUNT — THEY'RE WRECKING THE CAMP!

Aunt Carla changed back into the shape of the dog, and—
YOUR DOG'S CHASED OFF THE COWS EASILY, MARGIE. I'M GLAD YOU BROUGHT IT ALONG.
SO FAR, SO GOOD. AUNT CARLA IS REALLY EARNING HER KEEP!

But, later—
PERFECT! A CLOUDBURST! NOW THEY'LL HAVE TO SHIFT. THAT CAMP-SITE WILL BE A MUD-BATH BEFORE LONG — HA, HA!

The farmer was right! Soon—
YIKES! WE'RE ANKLE-DEEP IN WATER, AUNT CARLA!
WE SHOULD HAVE REALISED THIS WOULD HAPPEN IF IT RAINED. NO WONDER THAT NASTY FARMER SUGGESTED IT! I THINK IT'S TIME I DEALT WITH THAT AWFUL MAN!

AUNT! WHAT ARE YOU GOING TO DO? WHY HAVE YOU CHANGED INTO AN OWL?
IT'S TIME THAT FARMER HAD A LITTLE SCARE, DEAR.

And so, minutes later—
WAKE UP, YOU WRETCH! WHO DO YOU THINK YOU ARE, TREATING THOSE CHILDREN SO BADLY?
WH-WHAT ON—? A TALKING OWL!

THE FAIRY-FOLK ENJOYED HAVING THE CHILDREN IN THEIR USUAL FIELD. UNLESS YOU ALLOW THEM TO RETURN, ILL-FORTUNE WILL BE YOUR LOT!
I-I DON'T BELIEVE THIS! IT — IT ISN'T HAPPENING—

When Carla got back—
DRY YOURSELF OFF AS BEST YOU CAN, CHILDREN! IT'LL SOON BE DAWN SO WE'LL MAKE OURSELVES A HOT DRINK AND THEN START SHIFTING THE TENTS.
WHAT HAPPENED?
I SPOKE TO THE FARMER, DEAR! I THINK THINGS WILL LOOK A LOT BETTER TOMORROW.

But—
FANCY GETTING ALL WORKED UP OVER A BAD DREAM! FAIRIES INDEED! TALKING OWLS! I'LL SHOW THOSE KIDS WHO'S BOSS!

So—
NO, YOU CAN'T HAVE EGGS OR MILK! GET OFF MY LAND BEFORE I SET THE DOGS ON YOU. GO INTO TOWN FOR YOUR STUFF!
BUT IT'S MILES INTO TOWN!
SO MUCH FOR TEACHING HIM A LESSON, AUNT! HE'S WORSE THAN EVER!
Later, Margie took her 'dog' for a walk and Carla was able to change back to her normal self—
TONIGHT, I'LL REALLY FIX HIM, MARGIE. AND IF THINGS GO AS THEY SHOULD, I THINK HE'LL BE GLAD TO HAVE YOU KIDS ON HIS LAND.
OH, AUNT CARLA, I GET WORRIED WHEN I SEE THAT LOOK IN YOUR EYE. I HOPE YOU KNOW WHAT YOU'RE DOING.
And so, in the small hours that night—
HECKATEY, PECKATEY, A LESSON HE'LL LEARN, WITH FLAME AND FIRE THAT DOES NOT BURN!
NOW TO CHANGE BACK INTO A DOG AND WAKEN THE FARMER.
IT — IT'S THE DOG THAT BELONGS TO THOSE KIDS! THANK GOODNESS HE WAKENED ME — MY HAY SHED'S ON FIRE! ALL THE WINTER FOOD FOR MY ANIMALS—
Carla raced back to the camp-site, and—
GET THE KIDS UP AND DO YOUR STUFF AT THE FARM, MARGIE. BUT THERE'S NO NEED FOR ALARM — MY FIRE ONLY SEEMS TO BURN!
O.K, AUNT. I'LL RAISE THE ALARM!
Soon—
I DON'T KNOW WHAT I'D'VE DONE WITHOUT YOUR HELP! LOOKS LIKE WE'LL SAVE THE HAY, MA'AM! THE FIRE'S DYING DOWN ALREADY!
AS YOU CAN SEE, MY CHILDREN AREN'T AS BADLY BEHAVED AS YOU SUPPOSED!
TIME TO REMOVE THE HARMLESS FLAMES, I THINK!

When the 'flames' had died away—
I CAN'T THANK YOU ENOUGH. TOMORROW YOU MUST ALL MOVE BACK TO YOUR USUAL SITE.
GOOD OLD AUNT CARLA. SHE'S EVEN WAGGING HER TAIL!
But, as they moved back to the camp-site—
WHERE ARE YOU GOING, AUNT? WHAT ARE YOU UP TO?
JUST GOING TO MAKE SURE HE DOESN'T HAVE A CHANGE OF HEART, DEAR. I SHAN'T BE LONG!
A little later—
THAT'S FUNNY! THERE'S NO SIGN OF ANY BURNING AT ALL! THE HAY ISN'T EVEN SCORCHED!
I THOUGHT HE MIGHT NOTICE SOMETHING STRANGE—
HECKATEY, PECKATEY, BARN AND FARM-HOUSE, I CHANGE MYSELF INTO A LITTLE FIELD-MOUSE!
THAT WAS JUST 'FAIRY-FIRE', MR FARMER — A WARNING FROM THE LITTLE FOLK. MAKE SURE THE CHILDREN HAVE A HAPPY HOLIDAY, AND THINGS WILL GO WELL FOR YOU IN FUTURE.
OH, GOOD GRIEF! THAT OWL WASN'T A DREAM AFTER ALL!
Later that day, the kids received an invitation from the farmer to a slap-up lunch!
EAT UP, KIDS! AND TONIGHT WE'LL HAVE A BARBECUE AND A SING-SONG! YOU'LL WANT FOR NOTHING WHILE YOU'RE ON MY FARM!
THREE CHEERS FOR THE FARMER! HIP-HIP-HOORAY!
YOU DID IT AGAIN, AUNT CARLA! YOU 'HOUNDED' THE FARMER WITH 'DOGGED' DETERMINATION, HA, HA! HAVE SOME OF THIS DELICIOUS HOME-MADE PIE!

THE FOUR MARYS

MARY Field, Mary Cotter, Mary Simpson and Mary Radleigh were in the Third Form at St Elmo's School for Girls, and were good friends. One day, a special ceremony was held at the school sports pavilion for the opening of a new extension which had been built by Mr Lentham, father of Third Form snob, Mabel.

Dr Gull, the Headmistress, then called for the inaugural sports meeting to begin —

Three other teams had been invited to the special meeting — old rivals, Grant's Academy and Thorncliffe High, and a team from the nearby village of West Mead.

The village girls were very shy at first.

The first event was the 4 x 100 metres relay. The Marys were representing St Elmo's. School snobs, Veronica Lavery and Mabel Lentham looked on.

The village girls were not as fast as the Marys, but their baton-changing was superb.

At the final changeover, Grant's dropped their baton and Mary Field had to stop and restart. But the West Mead girls changed baton perfectly.

THE PEASANTS HAVE WON. SERVES THE FOUR MARYS RIGHT!
YES, BUT THEY'RE LETTING DADDY DOWN. HE'S ALSO GIVING A CUP, YOU KNOW. HE WON'T WANT IT TO GO TO A MOB OF VILLAGE PEOPLE!

YOUR BATON-CHANGING WAS SUPERB. THAT'S WHAT BEAT US.
COME AND MEET OUR COACH, DR ROBERTSON. SHE'S A REAL SPORTS FIEND.

YOU MUST BE SOME COACH, DR ROBERTSON. WERE YOU A PROFESSOR OF ATHLETICS?
OH, NO. ATHLETICS IS MY HOBBY. I LECTURED IN LANGUAGES AT OXLEIGH.

Though the West Mead girls won the relay, St Elmo's won most of the individual events, and narrowly took the Lentham Trophy.
YOU PUT UP A TERRIFIC SHOW, GIRLS. WELL DONE. WE'RE HAVING TEA IN THE NEW EXTENSION. WILL YOU COME AND JOIN US?
YOU'VE GOT A SUPER NEW EXTENSION — AND WE'RE LOSING OUR TRAINING FIELD. IT ISN'T FAIR. SIR WILLIAM SMITHERS HAS SOLD IT TO A BUILDER.

BUT YOU TRAIN ON THE MEADOW. THAT'S COMMON GROUND. THEY CAN'T BUILD ON THAT.
IT'S TRUE IT WAS USED AS COMMON LAND FOR CENTURIES, MARY, BUT SIR WILLIAM CLAIMED IT, AND NOW HE'S SOLD IT. SOME SORT OF LEGAL FIDDLE, I THINK.

Later —
WE'LL ASK THE HEAD IF YOU CAN TRAIN ON THE SCHOOL GROUNDS. WE SHOULD BE ABLE TO FIT YOU IN SOMEHOW!
THANKS VERY MUCH. WE'RE HOLDING A PROTEST MEETING TOMORROW NIGHT, NOT THAT IT'LL DO ANY GOOD. SIR WILLIAM WON'T CHANGE HIS MIND NOW.

IT'S MADDENING THAT THE WEST MEAD GIRLS SHOULD LOSE THEIR ONLY SPORTS FIELD JUST SO THAT SOME BUILDER CAN GET RICH QUICK!
I'LL HAVE YOU KNOW MY FATHER IS RICH ALREADY. ANYWAY, THE VILLAGERS DON'T NEED A COMMON. THEY'RE COMMON ALREADY!

SO IT'S MR LENTHAM WHO'S BOUGHT THE COMMON. HE GIVES US EXTRA SPORTS FACILITIES, AND TAKES THEM AWAY FROM THE VILLAGERS. THAT'S HARDLY FAIR.
LET'S GO TO THE PROTEST MEETING AND SUPPORT THE VILLAGE GIRLS.

Next evening, after prep —
WHAT'S IN THE PACKAGE, RADDY?
YOU'LL SEE WHEN WE GET TO THE VILLAGE, FIELDY.

At West Mead —
SAVE OUR COMMON
GLAD YOU COULD COME, GIRLS. SIR WILLIAM SMITHERS AND MR LENTHAM ARE BOTH COMING, SO WE'RE GLAD OF YOUR SUPPORT.

HOW'S THIS FOR A PROTEST PLACARD?
WEST MEAD NEEDS THE MEADOW
GREAT, RADDY. BUT I HOPE YOU'RE NOT PLANNING TO THROW EGGS AS WELL!

HAVEN'T YOU SPELT BUNGALOWS WRONGLY, RADDY?
NO WAY. FOR LENTHAM HOUSES, THE SPELLING'S RIGHT!
SPORT NOT BUNGLE-OWES

At last Sir William Smithers arrived, with Mr Lentham and a lawyer —
STEALING SPORTS-FIELDS ISN'T CRICKET
THERE ARE ST ELMO'S GIRLS AMONG THE PROTESTORS, SIR WILLIAM. I'LL HAVE WORDS WITH DR GULL ABOUT THIS LATER!

Mr Lentham's lawyer spoke to the meeting —
AS YOU ALL KNOW, THE FIELD KNOWN AS THE MEADOW WAS USED AS A COMMON FOR CENTURIES. BUT IT ALWAYS BELONGED TO THE DUKE OF WESSEX, AND THE PRESENT DUKE SOLD IT TO SIR WILLIAM SMITHERS —
HE HAD NO RIGHT TO SELL COMMON LAND!

THE COMMONS REGISTRATIONS ACT OF 1965 REQUIRED ALL COMMON LAND TO BE REGISTERED BY JULY, 1972. WEST MEAD DID NOT REGISTER THE MEADOW AS A COMMON, SO IT CEASED TO BE A COMMON —
AND REVERTED TO THE DUKE OF WESSEX, WHO SOLD IT TO SMITHERS, WHO SOLD IT TO LENTHAM. THE VILLAGERS HAVEN'T A LEGAL LEG TO STAND ON!

Mr Lentham was next to speak —
I PLAN TO BUILD SIXTY HOUSES. THEY'LL BRING MONEY AND BUSINESS TO WEST MEAD, AND —
THEY'LL SPOIL THE VILLAGE. WILL YOU LIVE IN ONE OF THEM, MR LENTHAM?

The meeting broke up soon afterwards.
THANKS FOR TRYING TO HELP, MARY.
I DIDN'T DO MUCH. IT LOOKS AS THOUGH NOTHING WILL STOP MR LENTHAM BUILDING ON THE MEADOW NOW.

When the Four Marys got back to St Elmo's —
DR GULL WANTS TO SEE YOU, GIRLS.
OH, NO! I WONDER WHAT SHE WANTS?

In the Head's room —
MR LENTHAM HAS JUST TELEPHONED. HE SAYS THAT ST ELMO'S GIRLS — YOU — WERE INVOLVED IN A VILLAGE BRAWL.
EXCUSE ME, DR GULL, IT WASN'T A BRAWL — IT WAS A PROTEST MEETING.

DO NOT ARGUE WITH ME. YOU WILL ALL SPEND NEXT HALF-DAY IN THE LIBRARY, WRITING "ST ELMO'S YOUNG LADIES MUST BEHAVE WITH DIGNITY" — FIVE HUNDRED TIMES.

And two days later —
THIS IS A SUPER DAY TO BE STUCK IN HERE. THE OTHERS ARE OFF ON A HISTORY FIELD TRIP TO THE SITE OF THE BATTLE OF LONG MEAD —
BETWEEN THE DANES AND THE SAXONS! NOW, THERE'S A THOUGHT. GOOD JOB I'VE FINISHED MY LINES!

Mary Simpson was the star history pupil in the Third Form.
COULD I PLEASE SEE THE BOX OF WESSEX PAPERS? WE WERE TOLD BY MISS CREEF THAT WHEN THE SCHOOL WAS A GREAT HOUSE IT BELONGED TO THE DUKE.
THE WESSEX PAPERS? YOU WILL TAKE GREAT CARE, WON'T YOU, MARY? THEY'RE VERY OLD, VERY FRAGILE — AND VERY VALUABLE.

WHAT ARE WE LOOKING FOR, SIMPY?
I'M NOT QUITE SURE, COTTY. THE OLDEST PARCHMENT WE CAN FIND.

Some time later —
THIS HAS THE WESSEX GRAND SEAL ON IT, AND IT'S IN LATIN — THAT LOOKS LIKE THE WORD "COMMON". COME ON, SIMPY, YOU'RE OUR STAR LATIN SCHOLAR.
I CAN'T MAKE THE REST OUT. IT'S LIKE NO LATIN I KNOW.

The librarian couldn't help.
SORRY, MARY, I'M NOT A LATIN EXPERT. WHY NOT ASK MISS CREEF? SHE MAY BE ABLE TO HELP. YOU CAN BORROW THE PARCHMENT.
THANKS, I'LL RETURN IT AS SOON AS I CAN.

WHAT WE NEED IS A REAL EXPERT — AND DR ROBERTSON WAS A LANGUAGES LECTURER AT OXLEIGH UNIVERSITY!
WELL, WE'VE ALL FINISHED OUR LINES. SO WHAT ARE WE WAITING FOR — LET'S GO TO SEE HER!

So, soon —
THE FOUR MARYS FROM ST ELMO'S. I THOUGHT YOU'D BE ON THE HISTORY TRIP TO LONG MEAD.
WE HAD TO STAY AT SCHOOL TO WRITE LINES. BUT WE FOUND THIS PARCHMENT IN THE LIBRARY—

In Dr Robertson's cottage —
NO WONDER YOU COULDN'T TRANSLATE IT, MARY. IT'S NOT LATIN — IT'S OLD ENGLISH. LEOFRIC, EARL OF ESSEX, GRANTS THE MEADOW TO THE PEOPLE OF WEST MEAD SO LONG AS THEY HAVE A "VAPNASCHAW" ONCE A YEAR. HE MUST HAVE DONE THAT AFTER THE BATTLE OF LONG MEAD.

THE WORD VAPNASCHAW MEANS A WEAPON-SHOWING. THE LORD COULD CHECK HOW MANY SOLDIERS HE HAD BY THIS MEANS.
SO, IF WE GATHER ON THE MEADOW AND SHOW WEAPONS TO THE PRESENT OWNER OF THE LAND, THE VILLAGERS CAN KEEP THE MEADOW FOR AT LEAST A YEAR!

BUT HOW DO WE GET THE VILLAGERS TO SHOW WEAPONS? AND HOW DO WE GET SIR WILLIAM SMITHERS AND MR LENTHAM THERE?
I CAN FIX ALL THAT. FIRST, I'LL PHONE DAD AT RADLEIGH HALL, THEN WE'LL SEE OUR VILLAGE FRIENDS, THEN WE'LL SEE DR GULL.

Next day, in Dr Gull's study —
THE WEST MEAD VILLAGERS ARE HAVING A PROCESSION, PAGEANT AND SPORTS TO CELEBRATE MIDSUMMER, DR GULL. CAN WE TAKE PART, AND CAN WE GET PERMISSION TO HOLD IT IN THE MEADOW?
WE ARE ALWAYS HAPPY TO HELP THE VILLAGERS, MARY. FORTUNATELY, MR LENTHAM CAME IN TO CHECK THE NEW PAVILION EXTENSION. PERMISSION FOR THE MEADOW IS UP TO HIM.

WELL, OF COURSE, LADY MARY, SO LONG AS IT'S OVER BY A WEEK ON SATURDAY. WE START BUILDING THE FOLLOWING MONDAY.
THANK YOU VERY MUCH, MR LENTHAM. AND, PLEASE, WILL YOU COME WITH SIR WILLIAM SMITHERS AS GUESTS OF HONOUR? DADDY — THE EARL OF RADLEIGH — IS DYING TO MEET YOU.
WHAT A FIB!

Mr Lentham agreed immediately, but Mary had one more thing to ask —
THE HIGHLIGHT OF THE DAY COULD BE KNIGHTS JOUSTING, IF SIR WILLIAM AND YOU WOULD PUT ON AN EXHIBITION. I'M SURE YOU ARE BOTH SUPER HORSEMEN, AND MY MOTHER, THE COUNTESS OF RADLEIGH, WOULD PRESENT A TROPHY TO THE WINNER. WE MIGHT EVEN GET A TV CAMERA ALONG.
MR LENTHAM WILL NEVER FALL FOR THAT. OH, MY HAT, BY THE LOOK ON HIS FACE, HE HAS!

Mr Lentham even agreed to find the proper costumes!
GOOD GRIEF, RADDY, YOU'RE OUTRAGEOUS! WE COULD HARDLY KEEP OUR FACES STRAIGHT.
THE MAN'S A TOTAL SNOB. WAVE AN EARL AND A COUNTESS AT HIM, AND HE'LL DO ANYTHING. COME ON, WE'VE GOT COSTUMES TO MAKE. DAD WILL SUPPLY ALL THE OTHER THINGS WE NEED FROM THE RADLEIGH HALL MUSEUM.

Ten days later, at the pageant —
THE FOUR MARYS ARE COMMON PEASANTS, VERONICA. BUT DADDY IS A KNIGHT AND I'M HIS SQUIRE.
AND I'M SIR WILLIAM'S PAGE. MAYBE WE'LL ADD SOME CLASS TO THIS AFFAIR!

When the Earl and Countess of Radleigh arrived —
HI, DAD! HI, MUM! GOT THE GEAR?
ALL YOU ASKED FOR, MARY. WHAT ARE YOU COOKING UP NOW, YOU RASCAL?

Sir William Smithers and Mr Lentham led the procession from the village hall to the Meadow —
THEY'RE FULL OF THEMSELVES JUST NOW, BUT THEY'RE IN FOR A SHOCK!

IT'S A SMASHING PARADE. THE VILLAGERS HAVE WORKED WONDERS.

The Meadow had been set up for the jousting match.
I HEAR SIR WILLIAM ISN'T VERY GOOD ON A HORSE. THE JOUSTING COULD BE A REAL RIOT, FIELDY!

Wessex TV had sent along a camera team.
CONCENTRATE ON MY DADDY. HE'S SURE TO WIN!

But the jousting was a disaster — for BOTH knights!
THEY'VE BOTH COME A CROPPER, HO, HO!

Next, an archery contest got under way. Then —
THIS IS WHERE I PUT ON MY CLOAK AND BECOME THE TOWN CRIER!

HEAR YE, HEAR YE, HEAR YE! THE WEAPON-SHOWING HAVING TAKEN PLACE IN VIEW OF THE LORD OF THE MANOR, THE MEADOW REMAINS FOR THE USE OF THE PEOPLE UNTIL THIS DAY, A YEAR FROM NOW — WHEN WE WILL SHOW WEAPONS AGAIN!

THE MEADOW REMAINS FOR THE PEOPLE? IT CAN'T! I'VE SOLD IT TO LENTHAM!
IT WASN'T YOURS TO SELL, SMITHERS. THERE'S AN ANCIENT RIGHT INVOLVED. DR ROBERTSON WILL EXPLAIN IT.

THE MEADOW WAS GRANTED ON CONDITION THAT AN ANNUAL WEAPON-SHOWING TOOK PLACE. THAT HAS JUST HAPPENED. YOU ACTUALLY TOOK PART IN IT.
MARY RADLEIGH DID THIS! SHE SET US UP, SIR WILLIAM!

THANKS A MILLION, RADDY. WE'VE GOT THE MEADOW FOR ANOTHER YEAR.
YOU'VE GOT IT FOR EVER, SO LONG AS YOU SHOW WEAPONS ONCE A YEAR. BUT YOU SHOULD REALLY THANK SIMPY. SHE FOUND THE PARCHMENT WHICH DOC ROBERTSON TRANSLATED. WHAT A GREAT DAY!

Then the sports started. The Earl of Radleigh refereed the tug-o'-war —
COME ON, MARYS. LET'S SEE IF YOU CAN WIN TWO BATTLES IN ONE DAY!

The Young Farmers' Club organised hay-tossing —
HEAVE IT OVER, LASS. THERE'S A KNACK TO IT.
YES — A KNACK I HAVEN'T GOT!

There was a catch-the-pig contest —
FANCY A BASH AT THAT, RADDY?
NO WAY! BESIDES, IF I CAUGHT IT, WE WOULDN'T BE ALLOWED A PET PIG AT ST ELMO'S. WE'VE GOT TWO ALREADY — VERONICA AND MABEL!

The final contest was a relay race round the Meadow — the village against St Elmo's.
NICE CHANGE! WE'RE IN THE LEAD!

The last runners couldn't be separated.
I DECLARE THE RACE A DEAD HEAT. WELL RUN, GIRLS.
SMITHERS AND LENTHAM WERE THE ONLY LOSERS TODAY.

The super day ended with a barbecue —
FOR A FEED LIKE THIS, WE'LL SHOW WEAPONS EVERY WEEK, CHUMS!
HA, HA! THANKS, MARYS! YOU GOT THE LENTHAM EXTENSION — BUT WE GOT THE LENTHAM EVICTION.

JUST SAY- AAAH!
THESE KING KONG FILMS ALWAYS MAKE ME CRY!
ANIMAL CRACKERS
I COULDN'T FIND AN APPLE, MR TELL!
I JUST HATE SCHOOL!
FUNNY SOMEONE'S TAKEN THE GLASS OUT OF THE MIRROR!
NOW LOOK HERE, SMALL FRY!
HE ALWAYS DID HAVE APPALLING MANNERS!

Nonie's Knight
NONIE BYRNE had a problem when Sir Ichabod, a medieval knight who she had disturbed from his centuries old sleep, set himself up as her guardian. When the first snow of the winter fell, Nonie decided to go sledging—
I'M GOING TO MEET THE GANG UP AT HOGSBACK HILL. WE'LL HAVE A GREAT TIME.
But Sir Ichabod had noticed Nonie setting out—
AH, LADY NONIE — YOU SHOULD NOT BE PULLING THIS HEAVY SLEDGE. SIT UPON IT, AND I SHALL BE HONOURED TO DRAW YOU THROUGH THE SNOW!
I'LL MANAGE O.K, SIR ICHABOD. YOU SHOULDN'T BE OUT IN THIS WEATHER — YOUR ARMOUR MIGHT GO RUSTY!
NAY, LITTLE DAMSEL, NOT A SPECK OF RUST WILL YOU FIND ON MY ARMOUR — OR MY WEAPONS! NOW, SIT ON YOUR SLEDGE!
I MAY AS WELL DO AS HE SAYS. IT'S TOO CHILLY TO STAND AROUND ARGUING.
COME ON, SIR ICH — FASTER!
HOGSBACK HILL
EGAD — A MONSTROUS WHITE GIANT STANDS IN OUR PATH! BUT FEAR NOT, LADY NONIE — I SHALL VANQUISH HIM!
BUT, SIR ICHABOD — IT'S ONLY A SNOWMAN!
But—
PREPARE TO FIGHT, O FAT WHITE ONE!
SIR ICHABOD! I'M SLIPPING DOWN THE HILL!

OOH — A WALL! GOT TO GET OFF!

LOOK — MY SLEDGE IS RUINED! AND ALL BECAUSE YOU CHALLENGED A HEAP OF SNOW TO A DUEL!
OH, LITTLE DAMSEL, I AM DESOLATE TO HAVE CAUSED YOU SO MUCH GRIEF! HOW CAN I MAKE AMENDS?

Soon—
SORRY ABOUT YOUR SLEDGE, NONIE! I SEEM TO REMEMBER YOU WON ALL THE RACES LAST YEAR!
MY SLEDGE MIGHT HAVE BEEN OLD, BUT IT CERTAINLY WAS FAST! I MAY AS WELL GO HOME!

I HAVE A WONDROUS INSPIRATION, LADY NONIE! WHY NOT USE MY SHIELD AS A SLEDGE? IT WILL BEAR YOU OVER THE SNOW AT GREAT SPEED!
O.K. IT'S WORTH A TRY.

GIVE ME A PUSH, WILL YOU, PLEASE?
CERTAINLY, LITTLE DAMSEL! MAY YOU HAVE A SAFE JOURNEY!

Nonie won every race!
YOU ARE FLYING LIKE A BIRD, LADY NONIE! IS ALL FORGIVEN?
IT CERTAINLY IS, SIR ICH — NO-ONE CAN BEAT ME ON YOUR SUPER-SHINY SHIELD!

Bunty's CUT-OUT and COLOUR WARDROBE

Using coloured pencils or crayons, colour the clothes in your favourite shades, then cut round the thick black lines and fit the clothes to the figure.

THE TEDDY BEARS' PICNIC

The very beautiful Longleat House.

IF you had gone down to Longleat on a very special August Monday, you wouldn't have been blamed for believing that "Every bear that ever there was, had gathered there for certain —" because it was indeed the day the Teddy Bears had their picnic!

Amy Cook finds a Rupert Bear display.

The picnic was the grand finale of a tour by the International Teddy Bear Club to raise money for the Save The Children Fund.

THERE were bears everywhere! Hundreds of them! As well as the ones on show, many of the visitors brought their own teddies along, too. And giant bears, tiny bears, old bears and young bears, dancing bears and famous bears like Rupert and Superted were peeping out from all corners.

THE VIBs (Very Important Bears) were out in force, too. These were bears which had been kindly loaned by a host of famous personalities, ranging from royalty and the world of politics to stars of stage, screen and TV.

Her Majesty The Queen had loaned her very own bear, and there was a special exhibition of royal bears.

THE proceedings were opened that morning by Ambassador Bear and for the rest of the day there was a great deal of fun for everyone. Clowns and magic tricks and a Punch and Judy Roadshow were just some of the attractions, along with the very exciting Parachuting Teddies.

Visitors could also take part in competitions, be made-up like clowns, have their own teddy bears valued by Bunny Campione of Sothebys — or perhaps buy a teddy at the Teddy Bears Auction.

Parachuting teddies — in the air—

Melissa Bussell and her boyfriend John Winspear with their collection of bears aged from 18-50 years.

— and on the ground!

MONDAY also saw the final of the National Bear of the Year contest. The winner of this turned out to be Old Bear, owned by eight-year-old Naomi Rodgeman of Warminster. Old Bear was thirty-four years old and had been given to Naomi's mother when she was a baby. Their prize was a seven day holiday in Berne, Switzerland.

It was a fine day indeed, enjoyed by the many visitors, as well as all the furry friends who came along to give their support to a very worthy cause.

Two happy collectors for the Save The Children Fund.

Amy finds a cuddly bear.

Vicky Lee had her face made-up by Micky The Clown.

Hannah Starkey has her teddy bear weighed while her sister Ruth looks on.

Amy enters a colouring competition.

Mr and Mrs Gould and their son David brought their dog Goliath, as well as their teddies.

Kerry Lawrence looks on as Nu Joan Crosbie does a few repairs. Joan runs a hospital for sick tedd in Dartford.

Amy makes friends with Rupert, Soccer Ted and Teddy Bear.

Magician Jumping Jack introduces his bear to Lord Christopher Thynne, owner of Longleat.

A teddy has its portrait done.

● The Royal Bear collection.

● Amy dances on stage with some friends.

A happy audience at the Punch and Judy Roadshow.

— then it's off for a ride on a Sinclair C5.

● Amy takes her teddy to see the largest bear in the world

● The final line-up in the Bear Of The Year Contest.

● And the winner — Old Bear with Naomi and her mum.

THE TEDDY BEARS' PICNIC

The Lost World
IT was the year 2020. Jane Tate and Jean Wilson were on their way to a history lesson. Like everyone else in their city they were trapped by the sizzling silver curtain that cut everyone off from the world outside. The gigantic force field ran through the school grounds.
DON'T YOU EVER WONDER WHAT THE WORLD IS LIKE BEYOND THE CURTAIN, JEAN?
I USED TO. BUT WHEN YOU KNOW IT'S CERTAIN DEATH TO VENTURE OUTSIDE, IT'S SILLY TO EVEN THINK OF ESCAPING.
PAGE TWO HUNDRED, GIRLS. TODAY WE SHALL LEARN WHAT IT WAS LIKE IN THE LATE TWENTIETH CENTURY. LIFE WAS VERY DIFFERENT TO WHAT IT IS TODAY.
PEOPLE TRAVELLED FREELY FROM CITY TO CITY, COUNTRY TO COUNTRY, AND FROM OUR PLANET TO OTHER WORLDS. DOES ANYONE KNOW WHAT FUEL WAS USED?
IT WAS OIL FOUND BENEATH THE EARTH'S CRUST.

ALL THESE FORMS OF TRANSPORT BURNT UP THE FUEL AT AN ALARMING RATE.
I WISH WE'D LIVED IN THOSE TIMES, JEAN. I'D LOVE TO FLY IN A PLANE.
THEN CAME THE TERRIBLE PLAGUE. A SPACE-SHIP RETURNED TO EARTH WITH A VIRUS THAT WAS DEADLY TO HUMANS. MILLIONS OF PEOPLE DIED. WE MUST BE ETERNALLY GRATEFUL TO THE WONDERFUL FORCE FIELD THAT HAS SAVED OUR LIVES.
BUT THAT WAS A LONG TIME AGO, MISS CRAWFORD. WHAT WOULD HAPPEN IF WE WERE TO GO OUTSIDE THE FIELD NOW?
WE KNOW NOTHING MORE ABOUT THIS MENACE, JANE. THE EXPERTS SAY THAT IT COULD BE HUNDREDS OF YEARS BEFORE THE PLAGUE HAS BURNT ITSELF OUT. TO VENTURE OUTSIDE IS CERTAIN SUICIDE, THAT EVERYONE KNOWS.
I DON'T THINK PEOPLE HAVE ANY FIGHTING SPIRIT LEFT THESE DAYS, JEAN.
WELL, WE DON'T HAVE ANY WARS LIKE THEY USED TO. YOU SHOULDN'T COMPLAIN, JANE.
YOU SHOULD HEAR MY GRANDFATHER'S TALES, JEAN. PEOPLE USED TO BE SO ADVENTUROUS. THEY WOULD CRAWL INTO HOLES UNDER THE EARTH'S CRUST, AND CLIMB UP MOUNTAINS INTO THE SKY JUST FOR THE FUN OF IT. NOW WE JUST DON'T TRY ANYTHING ANY MORE.
I WISH I HAD A GRANDFATHER. HE WAS KILLED BY THE MENACE.

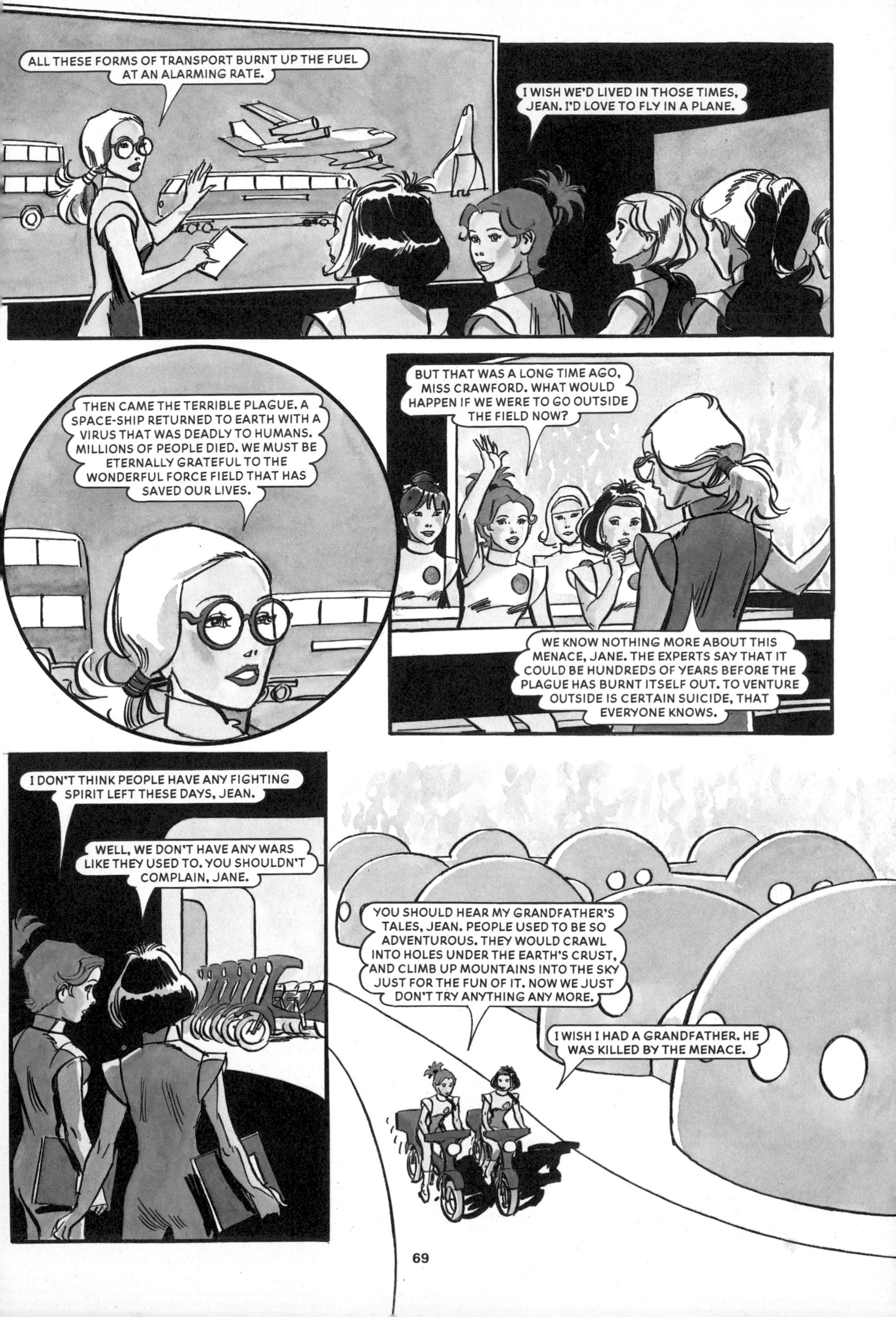

JEAN'S COME TO MEET GRANPA, MUM. SHE'S HEARD SO MUCH ABOUT HIM.
OH,DEAR! DON'T QUESTION HIM ABOUT THE PAST, JEAN — OR HE'LL GO ON FOR EVER.
THESE ARE STRANGE-LOOKING ORNAMENTS, MUM. WHAT ARE THEY FOR?
THEY'RE FLOWERS TO DECORATE OUR ROOM, DEAR. THE REAL ONES USED TO GROW IN GARDENS AND BLOOM IN THE SPRING. THEY CALLED THEM DAFFODILS.
HERE IS YOUR FOOD, GIRLS — TAKE ONE OF EACH TO COMPLETE YOUR DIET.
PILLS — HUH! WHEN I THINK BACK TO THE DAYS WHEN WE HAD PROPER MEALS, I COULD WEEP.
THAT WAS OUR CHRISTMAS DINNER.
WHAT'S THAT BIG BROWN THING IN THE CENTRE?
THAT WAS A TURKEY, LASS. I CAN STILL TASTE IT NOW, WITH CHESTNUT STUFFING AND CRISPY ROAST POTATOES. OH, IT FAIR MELTED IN YOUR MOUTH. NOW WE JUST SWALLOW A TASTELESS PILL — BAH!
NOW I'LL SHOW YOU SOMETHING THAT'LL REALLY OPEN YOUR EYES. BUT DON'T YOU TELL A SOUL OR I'LL BE IN TROUBLE WITH THE LAW.
OH, GRANPA, YOU ARE NAUGHTY. WHAT AM I TO DO WITH YOU?

OH! WHAT PLACE IS THAT?
IT'S LONDON, FORTY YEARS AGO! THAT'S WHAT THE WORLD IS LIKE OUTSIDE, ME LASSES!

DON'T TALK RUBBISH, GRANPA. LONDON WON'T BE LIKE THAT NOW. THERE ARE NO VEHICLES, NO PEOPLE, AND THE BUILDINGS MAY BE GONE TOO.
BAH! NO-ONE KNOWS BECAUSE NOBODY'S GOT THE GRIT TO FIND OUT.

DON'T YOU LISTEN TO HIM, GIRLS. MANY LIVES HAVE BEEN LOST IN USELESS ATTEMPTS TO ESCAPE. NOW IT'S AGAINST THE LAW.
WELL, IF I WERE YOUNGER I'D HAVE A GO, THAT I WOULD. PEOPLE HAVE GOT NO PLUCK NOW AT ALL!

THAT PICTURE OF LONDON WAS TERRIFIC, JEAN, BUT YOU KNOW WHAT MADE ME WANT TO ESCAPE MOST — IT WAS THOSE DAFFODILS. MY LAST WISH ON EARTH WOULD BE TO SEE A REAL ONE.
THE MENACE HAS PROBABLY WIPED OUT EVERY LAST ONE OF THEM, JANE.

THAT'S WHAT MAINTAINS THE FORCE FIELD. YOU'D NEVER GET THROUGH THAT ENERGY CURTAIN ALIVE, JANE.
NUCLEAR REACTOR KEEP OUT
YES I WILL. I'VE THOUGHT OF A WAY.

ABOVE THIS FORCE FIELD,THE SUN IS SHINING. HARD TO BELIEVE, ISN'T IT?
I'VE NEVER SEEN THE SUN, SO I DON'T THINK ABOUT IT.
THIS IS WHERE I SHALL MAKE MY ESCAPE. GRANPA'S GOT SOME OLD GARDENING TOOLS. WILL YOU HELP ME DIG A TUNNEL, JEAN?
OH, JANE, YOU'RE CRAZY! YOU WON'T LIVE TWO MINUTES.
AH, HERE'S AN OLD ANIMAL HOLE. THAT'LL HELP. I'LL START DIGGING TONIGHT. ALL I ASK OF YOU, JEAN, IS TO KEEP MY SECRET.
ALL RIGHT, I'LL HELP YOU DIG THE TUNNEL, BUT I STILL THINK YOU'RE MAD.
That night—
PHEW! THIS EARTH IS SOLID. WE'RE GOING TO BE EXHAUSTED, JEAN.
THIS IS AN OMEN THAT YOU SHOULDN'T GO, JANE. THIS PLAN IS JINXED FROM THE START!
HERE, HAVE SOME REFRESHMENTS!
THANKS, BUT I'D RATHER HAVE A SLICE OF TURKEY.
I MUST ADMIT THAT CHRISTMAS MEAL YOUR GRANPA SHOWED US LOOKED GOOD. EATING MUST HAVE BEEN AN ENJOYABLE RECREATION IN THOSE DAYS.

Later—
JANE! ARE YOU ALL RIGHT? YOU'VE GONE SO QUIET!
SURELY SHE WOULDN'T GO WITHOUT SAYING GOODBYE?

OH, JEAN, I'VE JUST SEEN DAYLIGHT AT THE END OF THE TUNNEL! IT WAS THE MOST BEAUTIFUL SIGHT I'VE EVER SEEN.
W-WHAT DID IT LOOK LIKE?

IT WAS STRANGE — ALL SORT OF MISTY AND GOLDEN. I COULDN'T SEE ANYTHING ELSE BUT THE SCENT OF THE AIR WAS FABULOUS!

GOODBYE, JEAN — WISH ME LUCK!
OH, I'M GOING TO MISS YOU SO MUCH.

THESE MAY BE MY LAST FEW MINUTES ALIVE. JEAN WILL TELL MUM AND GRANPA WHAT HAPPENED. I HOPE THEY WON'T BE TOO SAD.

MMM! THE AIR IS WONDERFUL. I MUST FILL MY LUNGS QUICKLY! THE WARMTH OF THE SUN UPON MY FACE — IT'S JUST LIKE HEAVEN!

I'M STILL ALIVE! A WHOLE MINUTE I'VE BEEN HERE AND — AARGH!

JEAN!
I — I DON'T KNOW WHAT CAME OVER ME, JANE. SUDDENLY I WAS FOLLOWING YOU.

EVERYTHING'S OVERGROWN. WE CAN HARDLY MOVE AT ALL!
IT'S A JUNGLE! THIS MUST BE WHAT THE WORLD WAS LIKE MILLIONS OF YEARS AGO!
W-WHATEVER'S THAT?
IT'S A THING CALLED A TREE. IT WON'T HURT YOU, JEAN. IT'S A GIANT PLANT — I'VE READ ABOUT THEM. SOME LIVE FOR HUNDREDS OF YEARS.
JEAN — LOOK! OH, I CAN HARDLY BELIEVE MY OWN EYES.
IT IS A DAFFODIL — A REAL ONE. JUST SMELL THE SCENT OF IT, JEAN.
SNARRRRL
EEEEK! WHATEVER'S THAT?

QUICKLY — UP THIS TREE! WE CAN HIDE IN THE BRANCHES.
IF IT'S THE MENACE — IT'LL GET US FOR SURE.
IT'S A TIGER! YEARS AGO THEY USED TO KEEP THESE ANIMALS IN ZOOS. NOW THEY'RE BREEDING WILD.
LET'S GO BACK, JANE. WE DON'T STAND A CHANCE. IF THE MENACE DOESN'T GET US THOSE ANIMALS WILL.
DON'T TALK ROT, JEAN. WE'RE STILL ALIVE. DON'T YOU REALISE WE'RE THE FIRST HUMANS TO SURVIVE OUTSIDE FOR AS MANY YEARS? WE'LL GO DOWN IN HISTORY!
WHAT ARE THESE BALLS, JANE?
I DON'T KNOW. WAIT A MINUTE — I'VE SEEN PICTURES OF THESE. THEY'RE APPLES!

DON'T, JANE — YOU'LL BE POISONED!
MMM! THEY TASTE FANTASTIC.
SCRUMPTIOUS! MMM! THIS IS WORTH ALL THE RISKS.
The taste of their first natural food gave the girls courage to journey on—
WE'VE COME TO THE END OF THE FOREST, THANK GOODNESS. WHAT ARE ALL THESE FUNNY LUMPS AND BUMPS, JANE?
I DON'T KNOW. LET'S LOOK INSIDE.
IT'S A BUILDING OF SOME SORT. OH, JEAN, THIS MUST HAVE BEEN A VILLAGE AT ONE TIME.
Suddenly—
GRRRRRRRR
WILD DOGS! RUN, JEAN!
NOW THERE ARE WILD PIGS! LET'S GET OUT OF HERE.

GRRRRR
SNORT
SNAP
SNARRRRL
PHEW! THAT WAS CLOSE.
LOOKS LIKE ALL THE DOMESTIC ANIMALS HAVE GONE WILD, TOO.
I WISH YOU'D TURN BACK, JANE. SOONER OR LATER OUR LUCK WILL RUN OUT.
JEAN, DO YOU REALISE WE'VE BEEN FREE FOR SEVERAL HOURS NOW AND WE'RE PERFECTLY WELL? IN FACT, I'VE NEVER FELT BETTER.
THEN WHAT'S HAPPENED TO THE MENACE, JANE? DOES IT MEAN THAT OUR WORLD IS SAFE ONCE MORE?
WE WON'T KNOW FOR SURE UNTIL WE'VE BEEN FREE FOR SEVERAL DAYS. JEAN, I'VE GOT A GREAT IDEA. LET'S CAPTURE AND TAME A WILD HORSE.
OH, JANE — MUST WE?
I ONCE READ IN A HISTORY BOOK THAT HORSES LOVE APPLES. WE'LL USE THESE FOR BAIT.

ISN'T HE A BEAUTY? HE COULD CARRY US BOTH EASILY.
I'D RATHER WALK ON MY OWN FEET, THANK YOU.

OH, JEAN, YOU HAVEN'T ANY SPIRIT AT ALL, HAVE YOU?
THAT'S NOT TRUE! I'D HAVE STAYED BEHIND THE FORCE FIELD, IF IT WAS!

HE'S QUITE TAME. I DON'T THINK IT WILL TAKE US LONG TO MASTER HIM, JEAN.

Two days later, at Jane's house—
THEY'VE GONE OUTSIDE THE FORCE FIELD. IT'S ALL YOUR FAULT, GRANPA, YOU PUT SILLY IDEAS INTO THOSE YOUNG GIRLS' HEADS.
HUMBUG! I BET THEY'RE HAVING A WONDERFUL ADVENTURE OUT THERE. I'M GOING UP TO THE VIEWING TOWER WITH MY BINOCULARS.

YOU WON'T SEE ANYTHING OUT THERE, OLD MAN. IT'S JUST A LIFELESS WILDERNESS.
WELL, I THOUGHT I SAW SOMETHING MOVING JUST NOW.
IT'S THEM! MY GRAND-DAUGHTER AND HER FRIEND ARE COMING BACK!

For the first time in many years, the force field was turned off—
OUR WORLD IS SAVED! THE MENACE HAS GONE!
HURRAY!
Some time later—
IT'S ALL THANKS TO YOU, GRANPA. IF YOU HADN'T TOLD US HOW WONDERFUL THE WORLD WAS, WE'D NEVER BE HERE NOW.
FORTY YEARS HENCE, SCHOOL CHILDREN WILL BE READING HOW TWO BRAVE GIRLS SHOWED THE WORLD HOW TO LIVE AGAIN. I'M PROUD OF YOU, MY LITTLE LASSES!

BEST IN SHOW
I say, you lot — what's all that din?
Can't a pup get any rest?
A fine rosette is nice to win,
But I think sleeping's best!

HAGGIS

SPRING

SUMMER

AUTUMN

WINTER

The ROCKHAVEN RESCUERS
A WEALTHY former pupil of Rockhaven Village School had left money to keep the school open on condition that the pupils, now all girls, provided a local sea and mountain rescue team. Team leaders Kathy Davies and Gwen Jones were working hard to get the team into shape.
IT WAS GOOD OF THE ARMY CADETS TO LET US USE THEIR TRAINING ASSAULT COURSE, KATHY.
I DON'T THINK NAN AND SALLY ARE ENJOYING IT MUCH, GWEN.
I'M STUCK! HELP!
ARRRRGH!
SOON HAVE YOU OUT, NAN.
HERE COMES MISS LEWIS TO JOIN IN THE FUN.
COME ALONG GIRLS! WE HAVE A REAL EMERGENCY BACK AT OUR SCHOOL!
WHAT'S WRONG, MISS LEWIS?

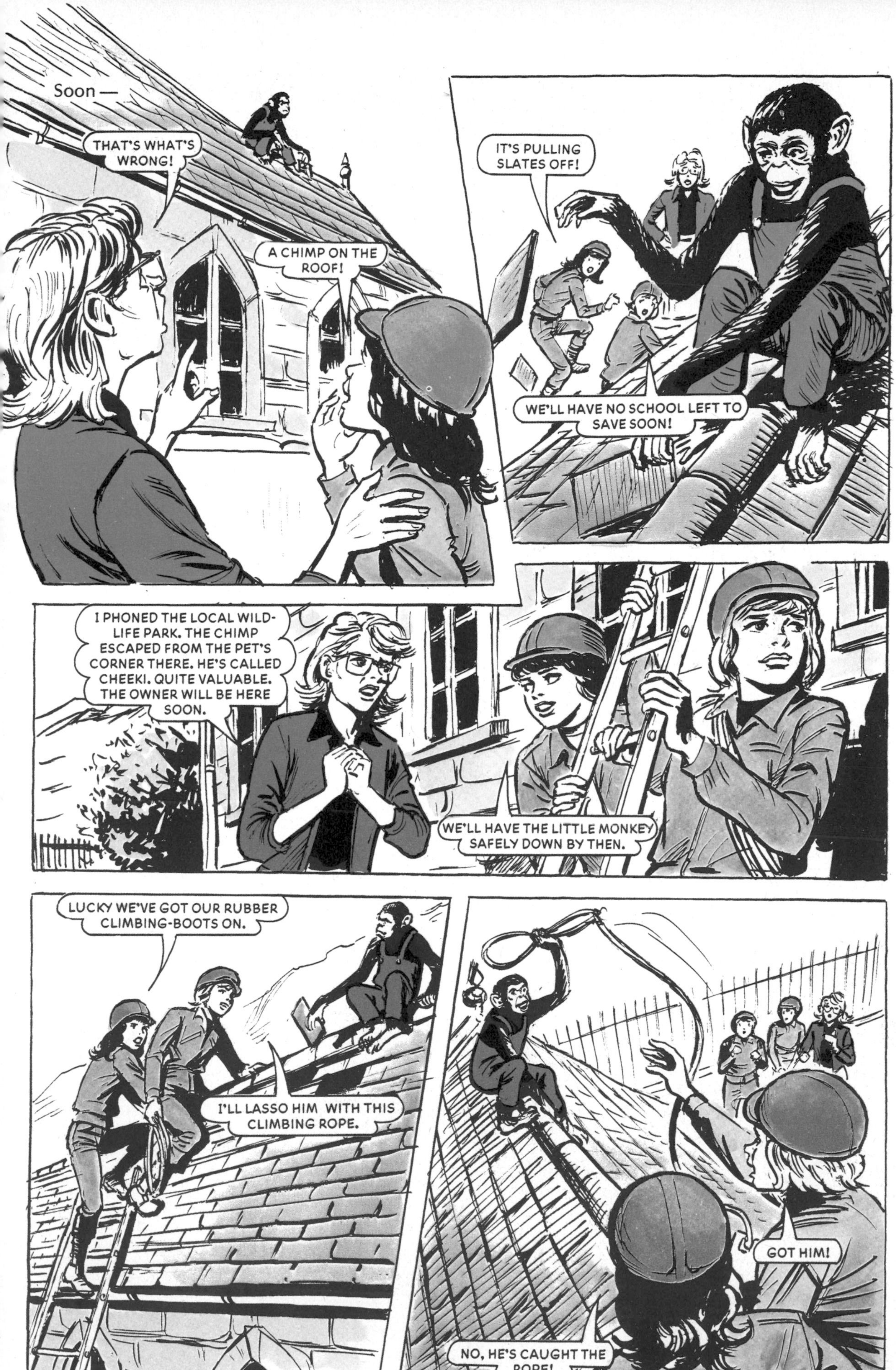

Soon —

THAT'S WHAT'S WRONG!

A CHIMP ON THE ROOF!

IT'S PULLING SLATES OFF!

WE'LL HAVE NO SCHOOL LEFT TO SAVE SOON!

I PHONED THE LOCAL WILD-LIFE PARK. THE CHIMP ESCAPED FROM THE PET'S CORNER THERE. HE'S CALLED CHEEKI. QUITE VALUABLE. THE OWNER WILL BE HERE SOON.

WE'LL HAVE THE LITTLE MONKEY SAFELY DOWN BY THEN.

NOW HE'S GOT YOU!
AAAH! I'M SLIDING OFF!
I'LL HOLD YOU!
LOOK OUT, SALLY! HE'S COMING DOWN THE LADDER.
Minutes later —
NOW HE'S HEADING OFF UP THE MOUNTAIN PATH.
WE'D BETTER GO AFTER HIM. CAN'T HAVE THE OWNER THINKING OUR RESCUE TEAM FAILED.
THE FRUIT IN THIS BAG SHOULD TEMPT HIM DOWN.
THEN I'LL BAG HIM IN THIS OLD FISHING NET.

THERE HE GOES!
HE CLIMBS BETTER THAN WE CAN!
COME ON DOWN, CHEEKI! NICE BANANAS AND TOMATOES!
URRGH!
SEEMS HE PREFERS BANANAS TO TOMATOES!
WE'LL GO UP AND GET HIM WITH YOUR NET, NAN, WHILE GWEN KEEPS HIM BUSY WITH BANANAS.
But soon —
THE LITTLE DEMON! THROWING BANANA SKINS DOWN FOR THEM TO SLIP ON!

HE'S COMING DOWN! QUICK, NAN! YOUR NET!
IT GOT ALL TANGLED UP FROM THAT FALL.
HE WENT THIS WAY!
MUST HAVE GONE DOWN THAT POTHOLE!
YOU GO FIRST, SALLY, THEN KATHY AND I WILL FOLLOW IF IT'S WIDE ENOUGH.
TIGHT SQUEEZE FOR YOU, NAN!
YOU'RE WELCOME! I'LL STAY UP HERE.
THERE'S WATER DOWN HERE.
BUT NO SIGN OF THE CHIMP!

Meanwhile —
HELP US BACK UP WITH THE ROPE!
RIGHT, GWEN!
OH, NO! I'M CAUGHT IN MY OWN NET!
NO! LEAVE THAT ROPE ALONE!
Next moment —
AARGH!
HE-ELP! GET US OUT!
HANG ON! I'M LOWERING THE SPARE ROPE.
ANYBODY HERE STILL FOND OF CHIMPS? WHERE IS HE NOW?
HE RAN OFF WHILE I WAS HELPING YOU UP.

Just then —
DISTRESS FLARE SIGNALS OUT AT SEA! WE'D BETTER GET BACK TO THE HARBOUR!
WHAT ABOUT THE CHIMP?
HE'LL JUST HAVE TO WAIT. OUR LOCAL LIFEBOAT IS AWAY FOR REPAIRS SO OUR RESCUE BOAT MAY BE NEEDED.
THE FLARES CAME FROM A SAILING YACHT OFF RIPPER REEF ROCKS. BE CAREFUL! WIND'S BLOWING UP.
HEY! YOU'VE GOT A LATE PASSENGER!
GOT A NEW SKIPPER FOR YOUR BOAT, EH?
THAT WRETCHED CHIMP!
HE MUST HAVE FOLLOWED US!

HE'S TRYING TO TAKE OVER THE STEERING!
THIS TIME HE GOES IN THE NET!
GOT HIM! THAT'LL KEEP HIM OUT OF HARM'S WAY.
SAIL AHOY!
THIS IS NO WEATHER FOR SAILING BOATS!
THEY'RE STUCK BETWEEN THOSE ROCKS! WHY DON'T THE IDIOTS HAUL DOWN THEIR SAIL?
OUR SAIL RIGGING ROPES ARE STUCK ON THE TOP-MAST! WIND KEEPS DRIVING US FURTHER INTO THESE ROCKS. AND OUR ENGINE'S FAILED!
WE CAN'T TOW THEM OFF WITH THIS WIND BLOWING THEIR SAIL. GET A LINE ACROSS, NAN.

DROP ANCHOR! SECURE THE LINE!
THE CHIMP'S GOT LOOSE!
OH, NO! HE'S GOING ACROSS! I'LL HAVE TO GO AFTER HIM! TAKE OVER, KATHY!
EEEK! A HAIRY APE!
DON'T WORRY! HE'S HARMLESS! PHEW! LUCKY WE DID THAT ASSAULT COURSE TRAINING!
THE ROPES WILL HAVE TO BE CUT UP THERE!
BUT WHO CAN CLIMB A SLIPPERY MAST?
HERE'S WHO! YOU UNTIED OUR ROPE AT THE POTHOLE CAVE, CHEEKI, SO GET UP THERE AND UNTIE THAT LOT!

HE'LL NEVER DO IT!
WELL, IF HE DOESN'T WE'LL JUST HAVE TO CHOP DOWN YOUR MAST AND CUT LOOSE ALL YOUR ROPES AND SAILS!

But soon—
HE'S DONE IT! HAUL DOWN THE SAIL!
YOU'RE A REAL SAILOR, CHEEKI!
MERMAID

YOU CAN PULL US OUT NOW, AND TAKE US BACK TO THE HARBOUR.

Later, back at the school—
THIS IS MR BROWN FROM THE WILD-LIFE PARK. HE'S MAKING A GENEROUS DONATION TO OUR FUNDS FOR RETURNING THE CHIMP SAFELY.
SO ARE THOSE LADIES WHOSE YACHT WE RESCUED, MISS LEWIS!
THANKS, CHEEKI! I RECKON YOU'D MAKE A SUPER NEW RECRUIT FOR OUR RESCUE TEAM!

QUEENIE JONES was football mad. Her brother, Jim played for Feltham Hearts, a youth club team. Queenie was their greatest fan.

OH, NO! THAT'S THEIR THIRD GOAL. THE HEARTS ARE WELL BEATEN AGAIN.

The Queen ♥f Hearts

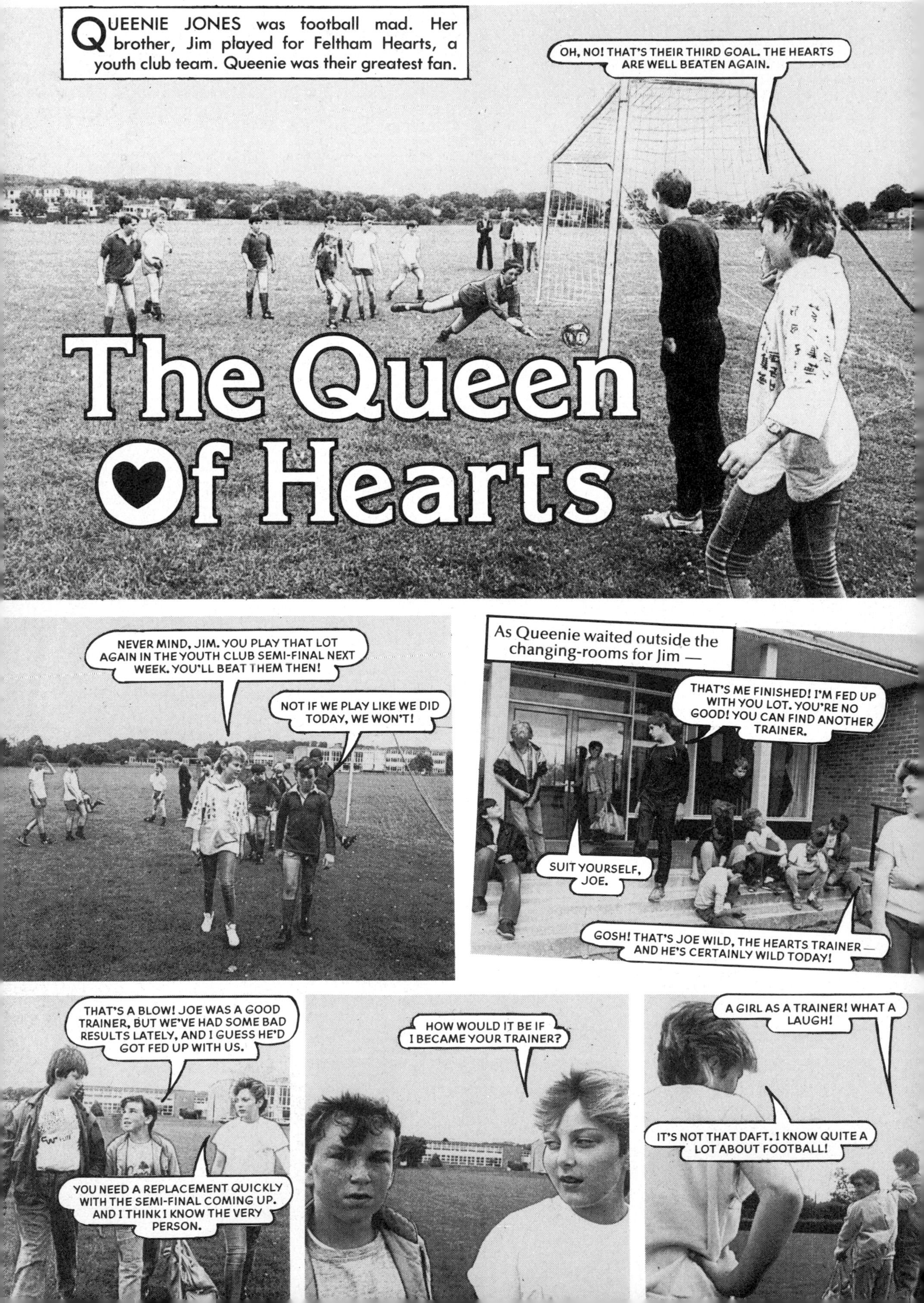

HO, HO, HO! SHE REALLY IS A SCREAM!
BOYS! THEY THINK THEY KNOW EVERYTHING!

Next day—
SAY WHAT THEY LIKE, THE BOYS ARE LOST WITHOUT JOE WILD. THEY REALLY NEED SOMEBODY TO SPARK OFF THEIR INTEREST AGAIN.

THROW THE BALL BACK, QUEENIE!

NOW FOR SOME BALL JUGGLING!
GOLLY! WHO'D HAVE THOUGHT A GIRL COULD DO THAT?

COME ON, THEN! LET'S SEE YOU TAKE IT OFF ME!

WOW! WHAT A BODY SWERVE!

WHAT A SHOT!

THAT'S GOT THEM THINKING!
O.K, QUEENIE! YOU'RE IN! YOU CAN BE OUR TRAINER FOR — ER — A TRIAL PERIOD.

And so—
COME ON, YOU LOT! NO SLACKING!
PHEW! SHE CERTAINLY KEEPS YOU AT IT.

WHAT'S WRONG WITH YOU? YOU'VE ONLY DONE TWENTY PRESS-UPS! KEEP IT GOING!

A few days later—
THAT'S BETTER! AT LEAST THEY'VE GOT THEIR ZEST FOR THE GAME BACK AGAIN.

On the day of the match—
I HOPE THEY GET A GOOD RESULT TODAY!

Then disaster struck —
OOH! MY ANKLE!

IT'S NO GOOD, QUEENIE. IT'S A SPRAIN! I WON'T BE ABLE TO PLAY.
THAT'S A GREAT START! A SEMI-FINAL WITHOUT OUR TOP STRIKER. WHAT DO WE DO NOW?

Queenie had the answer!
THEY'VE GOT A GIRL PLAYING FOR THEM!

The opposition soon found that the Hearts were no walk-over.
QUEENIE'S PLAYING WELL.

Queenie didn't hold back in the tackle either—
GREAT TACKLE, QUEENIE!

With five minutes to go, there was no score. Then —
GO, CHARLIE! DOWN THE WING!

And when Charlie's cross came over—
GOAL! WELL DONE, QUEENIE!

That was the winning goal—
GREAT, QUEENIE! WE'RE IN THE FINAL. JUST FOR THAT I'LL TREAT YOU TO THE YOUTH CLUB DISCO TONIGHT!

Later—
OF COURSE, YOU WON'T BE ABLE TO PLAY IN THE FINAL. SAM'S ANKLE WILL BE BETTER BY THEN!
I DON'T CARE ABOUT THAT. SEEING THE TEAM IN THE FINAL IS REWARD ENOUGH FOR ME.

I'VE ENTERED YOU FOR THE MISS YOUTH CLUB COMPETITION AS MY WAY OF SAYING THANKS. NOT THAT THERE'S MUCH CHANCE OF YOU WINNING!

But Jim was wrong.
THE WINNER — MISS QUEENIE JONES!
MISS YOUTH CLUB

And one of her first jobs as Miss Youth Club was to kick-off in the final of the Cup —

And to finish off a perfect day, Feltham Hearts won the cup!
THEY'VE WON! YIPPEE!

SUPERLAMB
A LOST and injured lamb had been saved by Mary Morgan, "rebuilt" by vet scientists, then given to her as a pet with bionic super-powers.
MAY AS WELL PUT MY OLD TOBOGGAN SLED AND MY LAMB TO GOOD USE IN THIS SNOWY WEATHER!
BAAA!
WE'RE STILL STUCK! PUSH HARDER!
I'D STOP AND HELP THEM BUT I'M LATE ALREADY FOR WORK AT GRUMPY MRS GRIMSHAW'S HOUSE.
PLAYING ABOUT WITH THAT SLED AND YOUR SILLY LAMB INSTEAD OF GETTING HERE ON TIME! I SOMETIMES WONDER IF YOU YOUNGSTERS REALLY WANT PART-TIME JOBS!

CLEAR THE SNOW FROM MY FRONT GARDEN PATH THEN CLEAN UP THE KITCHEN.
MRS GRIMSHAW'S OFF TO SEE THE PLUMBER ABOUT HER FROZEN PIPES.

DON'T GET LOST IN THE SNOW, LENNY! PHEW! THIS IS HARD WORK! WISH YOU COULD HELP ME — BUT I DON'T SEE HOW.

Just then—
THE SNOW'S MELTING! LENNY'S DOING IT WITH HIS BIONIC HEAT POWERS!

Soon—
CLEVER LAMB! YOU'VE MELTED ALL THE SNOW OFF THE PATH FOR ME!
BAAA!
I'LL SWEEP THE FLOOR FIRST, THEN DO THE DISHES SOMEHOW.

Then, in the house—
BRRR! IT'S COLD IN THIS KITCHEN! HOW AM I SUPPOSED TO CLEAN UP WHEN THE WATER PIPES ARE ALL FROZEN?

Moments later—
OH, NO! LENNY'S BIONIC HEAT HAS THAWED OUT THE FROZEN PIPES AND THEY'VE BURST!
HE'S DONE IT! FEELS LIKE A DEEP-FREEZE IN HERE NOW!

I CAN'T FIND THE STOP-COCK TO TURN OFF THE WATER! CAN YOU FREEZE IT ALL UP AGAIN, LENNY?
Not long after—
MRS GRIMSHAW'S BACK WITH THE PLUMBER!
LOOK OUT! THE FLOOR'S ALL ICY!

OOOF!
OH, GOSH!
EEEAAAH!

THAT'LL PUT A FEW POUNDS ON MY BILL!
WRETCHED GIRL! DID YOU TURN A HEATER ON IN HERE?
NO — ER — NOT EXACTLY, BUT—

I'VE CLEARED YOUR PATH AND YOU STILL OWE ME FOR LAST WEEK'S ODD JOBS!
THAT CAN PAY FOR THE CROCKERY YOU BROKE! CLEAR OFF!

ANOTHER PART-TIME JOB GONE!

SOMEBODY ELSE STUCK ON THIS HILL. WE'RE IN NO HURRY NOW, SO WE'LL GIVE HER A HAND.

I'LL PUSH WHILE YOU DRIVE.
IT'S KIND OF YOU, BUT I DOUBT IF YOU'LL MANAGE.

IT'S MOVING!
THANKS TO LENNY! HE'S DOING MOST OF THE PUSHING!

DOGS!
OH, DRAT! THAT DOOR'S COME OPEN AGAIN!

POPPY AND PENNY HAVE RUN OFF! THEY ALWAYS GET UPSET WHEN I TAKE THEM TO THE VET. THEY'LL TAKE SOME CATCHING NOW!

THEY MUST BE VALUABLE DOGS. GO GET THEM, LENNY!

GOSH! I'VE NEVER SEEN A LAMB RUN SO FAST!

THAT'S IT, LENNY! CHASE THEM BACK!
WELL, I NEVER!

WHAT A STRANGE LAMB! YOU MUST BRING IT ALONG TO THIS AFTERNOON'S SHOW. IT'LL BE STARTING SOON AND I CAN GET YOU IN FREE.
WELL — THANKS! WE'VE NOTHING ELSE TO DO.
But —
IT'S AN ICE SHOW! I THOUGHT YOU MEANT A DOG SHOW!
GRAND ICE SHOW
SPECTACULAR
OH, NO! I'M RITA SHAW. MY HUSBAND MANAGES THE VARIETY SHOW AND I HAVE A PERFORMING DOGS ACT.
Soon—
I'D LIKE YOU TO SEE THIS LAMB, DEAR.
LATER, RITA! WE'RE PUTTING YOUR ACT ON AGAIN, NOW THAT WE KNOW THOSE TWO DOGS AREN'T ILL. GIVE YOUR YOUNG FRIEND A RINGSIDE SEAT.
GIVE US OUR BALL BACK!
THAT SEA-LION'S ALMOST AS CLEVER AS YOU, LENNY!
BAAAA!
I SHOULDN'T HAVE SAID THAT! NOW LENNY'S GOING TO SHOW OFF!
OOOF!

HE'LL RUIN THE SHOW!

GET OFF THE ICE! WE CAN'T COMPETE WITH THAT WOOLLY CLOWN! SEND ON THE DOG ACT!

I'LL HAVE TO GO AND FIND LENNY. CAN'T HAVE HIM UPSETTING THAT NICE LADY'S DOG ACT AS WELL.

STOP THAT AND COME HERE, LENNY!
BAAA!

NOW HE'S STOPPING THE DOG SLED! OOOF! I CAN'T GET ACROSS THIS ICE TO CATCH HIM!

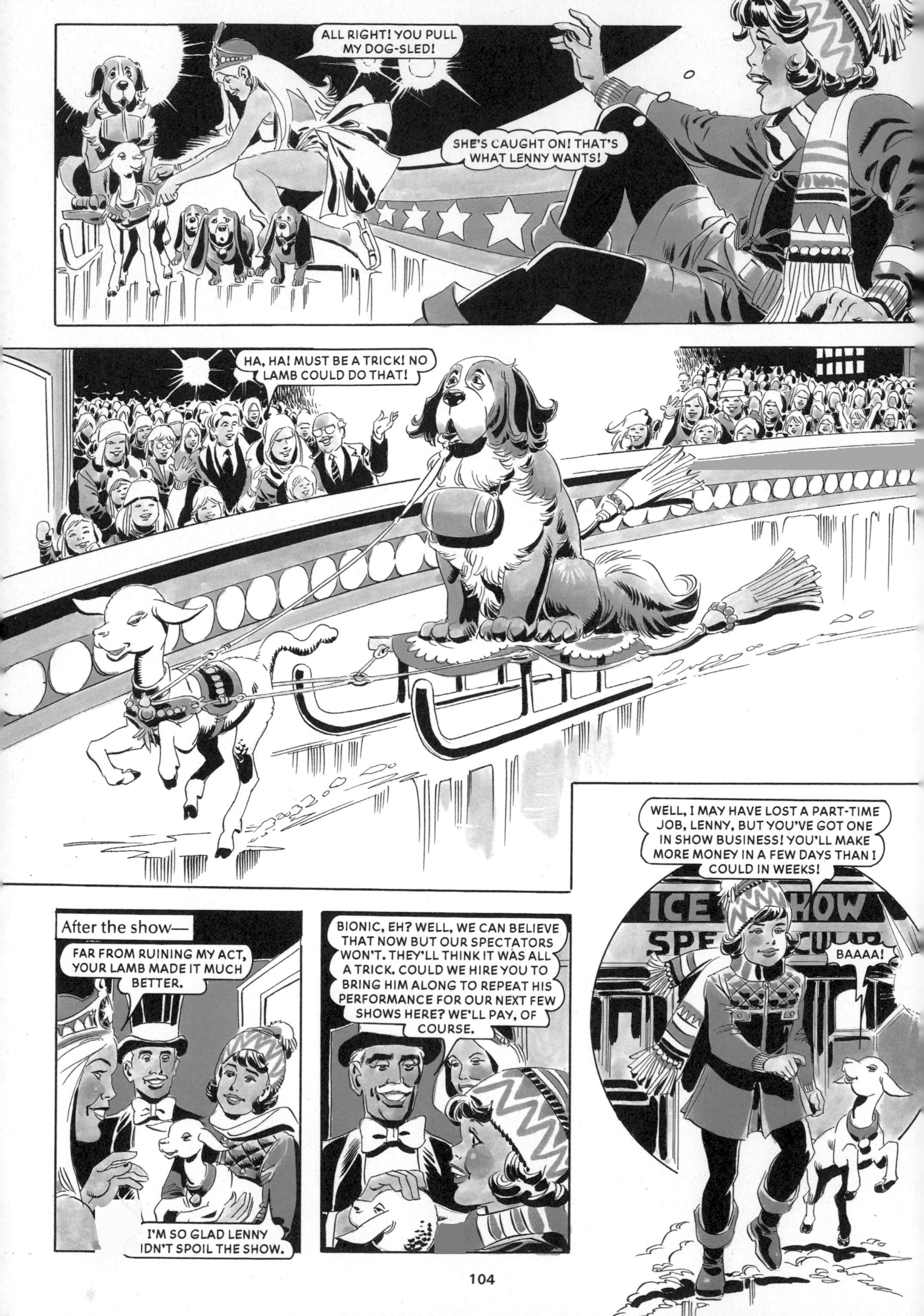

HA, HA! MUST BE A TRICK! NO LAMB COULD DO THAT!

The House of No Dolls

A Tale from the Toy Museum

"There was a little girl called Elizabeth Mallory, and she lived with her granny in a small village, just like you, m'dear."
THIS IS A SPECIAL BREW, ELIZABETH, TO CURE A COLD IN THE CHEST, WEAK EYESIGHT, OR EVEN BALDNESS IF IT'S RUBBED ON THE SCALP. ONE DAY I'LL TEACH YOU THE SECRETS OF MY HERBAL CURES.
OOH, PLEASE DO, GRANNY — THEN I'LL BE AS WISE AS YOU, AND EVERYBODY IN THE VILLAGE WILL LOOK UP TO ME!
THE FOLKS AROUND THESE PARTS SEEM MORE FRIGHTENED OF GRANNY THAN ANYTHING. SOME EVEN SAY SHE'S A WITCH, BUT THAT'S NONSENSE! I DON'T KNOW WHAT I'D DO WITHOUT HER. SHE'S ALL I'VE GOT LEFT SINCE MA AND PA DIED.
"But poor Elizabeth was soon to suffer yet another sad loss. Her granny became ill and none of her herbal remedies seemed to help"
ISN'T THERE ANYTHING I CAN GET YOU THAT WILL HELP, GRAN, DEAR? JUST TELL ME WHAT TO DO — AND I'LL DO IT!
THERE'S NOTHING THAT WILL HELP ME NOW, LITTLE ONE! I'M AN OLD WOMAN, AND MY TIME HAS COME. BUT I WORRY ABOUT WHAT'S TO BECOME OF YOU!
WHEN I'M GONE, YOU MUST GO TO SEE THE VICAR. ASK HIM IF HE'LL HELP YOU FIND YOUR MA'S SISTER — LUCY. SHE AND YOUR MA HAD A FOOLISH QUARREL YEARS AGO AND LOST TOUCH WITH EACH OTHER.
OH, GRAN DON'T SAY THINGS LIKE THAT! DON'T LEAVE ME — PLEASE DON'T DIE!
"Elizabeth's granny died the next day, and the poor child spoke to the vicar after the funeral."
I'VE ALREADY SEARCHED FOR THIS AUNT LUCY OF YOURS, ELIZABETH — YOUR GRANNY MENTIONED HER TO ME ONCE BEFORE. I'M SORRY TO TELL YOU THAT I'VE DISCOVERED THAT SHE MARRIED AND WENT ABROAD SOME YEARS AGO AND HAS NOT BEEN HEARD FROM SINCE.
B-BUT WHAT'S TO BECOME OF ME, VICAR? SHALL I HAVE TO GO TO THE ORPHANAGE?

NO, NO, MY CHILD — OF COURSE NOT! I HAVE MANAGED TO TRACE YOUR FATHER'S HALF-BROTHER, YOUR UNCLE CARL. THEY WILL GIVE YOU A HOME!
I-I SEE! PA DID MENTION UNCLE CARL, OF COURSE, B-BUT HE DIDN'T TELL ME A LOT ABOUT HIM.
THOUGH WHAT HE DID SAY WASN'T GOOD. HE AND PA DIDN'T GET ON WELL.
"When Elizabeth arrived at her uncle's house, she was not made welcome."
IF YOU PLEASE, I AM ELIZABETH MALLORY, AND I HAVE COME TO LIVE WITH MY AUNT AND UNCLE. ARE THEY AT HOME?
HUH — SO YOU'RE THE BRAT, ARE YOU? THIS'LL MEAN A LOT OF EXTRA WORK FOR ME AND THE HOUSEKEEPER, MRS JENNINGS! I SUPPOSE YOU'D BETTER COME IN.
YOUR ROOM'S AT THE TOP OF THE STAIRS! YOUR AUNT AND UNCLE ARE OUT AND WON'T BE BACK UNTIL LATE.
WHAT AN UNFRIENDLY GIRL! I HOPE UNCLE CARL AND AUNT LEONIE ARE MORE WELCOMING!
But, next morning—
I WANT TO MAKE IT CLEAR TO YOU, ELIZABETH, THAT I HAVE OFFERED YOU A HOME WITH THE GREATEST RELUCTANCE. YOUR AUNT AND I DO NOT CARE FOR CHILDREN.
I-I SEE. B-BUT MAYBE I COULD MAKE MYSELF USEFUL TO AUNT LEONIE. SO THAT I SHALL NOT BE SUCH A BURDEN ON YOU.
YOU'LL MAKE YOURSELF MOST USEFUL BY KEEPING OUT OF MY WAY! I WOULD PREFER YOU TO STAY IN THE UPPER PART OF THE HOUSE SO THAT WE DO NOT MEET MORE OFTEN THAN WE NEED TO.
"So Elizabeth kept well away from her aunt and uncle. One day, when she was exploring in the attic —"
OH, HOW WONDERFUL! AN OLD DOLLS' HOUSE, AND IT'S JUST LIKE THE HOUSE I'M LIVING IN!

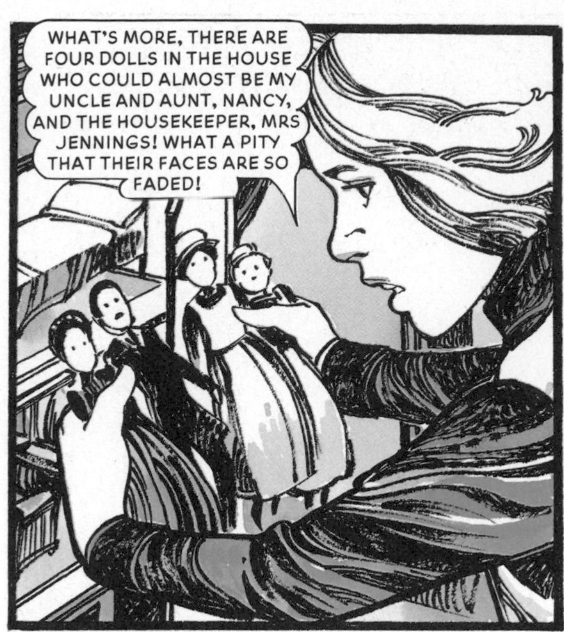
WHAT'S MORE, THERE ARE FOUR DOLLS IN THE HOUSE WHO COULD ALMOST BE MY UNCLE AND AUNT, NANCY, AND THE HOUSEKEEPER, MRS JENNINGS! WHAT A PITY THAT THEIR FACES ARE SO FADED!

"Elizabeth spent much of her time playing with the house."
UNCLE SHALL SAY 'WHERE IS THAT WRETCHED GIRL ELIZABETH? IS SHE KEEPING OUT OF YOUR WAY, MY DEAR?' AND AUNT LEONIE WILL REPLY, 'YES, THANK GOODNESS, AND IF I NEVER SEE HER AGAIN I WILL BE HAPPY.' I AM SURE THAT IS HOW THEY MUST TALK ABOUT ME!

THERE, YOU HEARTLESS CREATURES — TAKE THAT! IT IS MY TURN TO BE CRUEL!

"A few days later —"
THAT'S STRANGE — I WAS SURE I LEFT MY LOCKET IN THIS BOX WHEN I HAD MY BATH YESTERDAY. I MUST ASK MY AUNT AND UNCLE IF THEY HAVE SEEN IT.

"But there was a shock awaiting Elizabeth —"
IT'S NO USE SNIVELLING, GIRL! I HAVE SOLD THE LOCKET TO HELP PAY FOR YOUR KEEP. I AM SICK OF YOU EATING OUR FOOD AND LIVING IN OUR HOUSE AND PAYING NOTHING IN RETURN!
OH, YOU CRUEL, CRUEL MAN! THAT LOCKET WAS ALL THAT I HAD LEFT TO REMIND ME OF MY PARENTS AND MY DEAR GRANNY! HOW COULD YOU DO SUCH A TERRIBLE THING?

GET OUT OF MY SIGHT, GIRL! YOUR WHINING IS GIVING ME A HEADACHE!
YOU WILL PAY FOR WHAT YOU HAVE DONE! I WILL HAVE MY REVENGE ON YOU, NEVER FEAR!

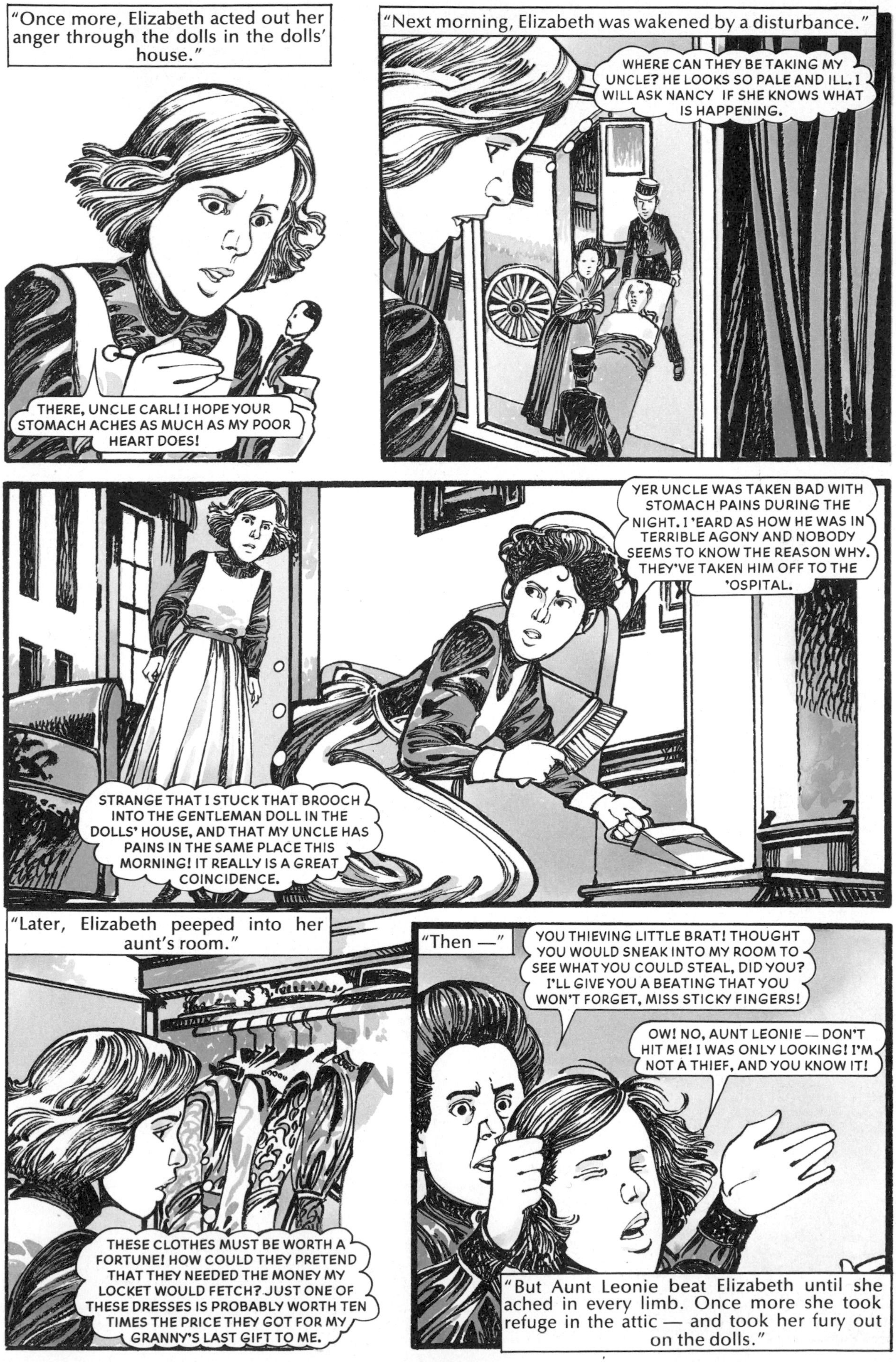

"Once more, Elizabeth acted out her anger through the dolls in the dolls' house."

"Next morning, Elizabeth was wakened by a disturbance."

YER UNCLE WAS TAKEN BAD WITH STOMACH PAINS DURING THE NIGHT. I 'EARD AS HOW HE WAS IN TERRIBLE AGONY AND NOBODY SEEMS TO KNOW THE REASON WHY. THEY'VE TAKEN HIM OFF TO THE 'OSPITAL.

STRANGE THAT I STUCK THAT BROOCH INTO THE GENTLEMAN DOLL IN THE DOLLS' HOUSE, AND THAT MY UNCLE HAS PAINS IN THE SAME PLACE THIS MORNING! IT REALLY IS A GREAT COINCIDENCE.

"Later, Elizabeth peeped into her aunt's room."

THESE CLOTHES MUST BE WORTH A FORTUNE! HOW COULD THEY PRETEND THAT THEY NEEDED THE MONEY MY LOCKET WOULD FETCH? JUST ONE OF THESE DRESSES IS PROBABLY WORTH TEN TIMES THE PRICE THEY GOT FOR MY GRANNY'S LAST GIFT TO ME.

"Then —"

YOU THIEVING LITTLE BRAT! THOUGHT YOU WOULD SNEAK INTO MY ROOM TO SEE WHAT YOU COULD STEAL, DID YOU? I'LL GIVE YOU A BEATING THAT YOU WON'T FORGET, MISS STICKY FINGERS!

OW! NO, AUNT LEONIE — DON'T HIT ME! I WAS ONLY LOOKING! I'M NOT A THIEF, AND YOU KNOW IT!

"But Aunt Leonie beat Elizabeth until she ached in every limb. Once more she took refuge in the attic — and took her fury out on the dolls."

THERE, AUNT LEONIE — TAKE THAT!
WHY AM I DOING THIS? I WOULD BE BETTER OFF THINKING OF A WAY TO GET MYSELF OUT OF THIS MISERABLE HOUSE. OH! WHAT WAS THAT NOISE DOWNSTAIRS?
"Elizabeth hurried down."
ELIZABETH — HELP ME! MY LEG — THE PAIN!
I WILL GET MRS JENNINGS TO CALL THE DOCTOR!
"Later —"
YOUR AUNT HAS A BROKEN LEG. I HAVE ARRANGED FOR HER TO HAVE A ROOM AT THE HOSPITAL WHERE YOUR UNCLE IS BEING TREATED. YOU SHOULD BE QUITE SAFE HERE WITH THE HOUSEKEEPER AND THE MAID TO LOOK AFTER YOU.
Y-YES, DOCTOR — THANK YOU.
WHAT HAPPENED TO MY AUNT IS VERY SHOCKING, AND I HAVE AN EERIE FEELING THAT HER ACCIDENT AND MY UNCLE'S ILLNESS HAVE SOMETHING TO DO WITH THE DOLLS AND THIS DOLLS' HOUSE.
"Later, in the kitchen —"
AND I TELL YOU, MY GIRL, THAT IT'S MY NIGHT OFF TONIGHT! I'VE ARRANGED TO GO AND SEE MY MARRIED SISTER OVER THE OTHER SIDE OF LONDON!
THAT'S NOT FAIR, MRS JENNINGS! IT'S MY NIGHT OUT AND YOU KNOW IT IS! I'M GOING, WHATEVER YOU SAY!
IT HARDLY MATTERS IN ANY CASE! WITH THE MASTER AND THE MISTRESS BOTH OUT OF THE WAY, I CAN SEE NO REASON WHY WE SHOULDN'T BOTH GO OUT!
B-BUT, MRS JENNINGS — I WILL BE HERE ALONE IF YOU AND NANCY BOTH TAKE A NIGHT OFF! I REALLY WOULD NOT DARE TO STAY BY MYSELF IN THIS BIG,OLD HOUSE!

"Despite Elizabeth's pleading, the servants left the house together."
I BEGGED THEM NOT TO LEAVE ME, BUT THEY JUST LAUGHED! I HATE THEM BOTH! HOW COULD THEY LEAVE ME ALONE HERE WHEN THEY KNOW I'M FRIGHTENED?

"Elizabeth went to the attic once more."
THERE, YOU WICKED THINGS! I SHALL SHAKE YOU UNTIL YOUR TEETH RATTLE! I HATE YOU! I HATE YOU BOTH!

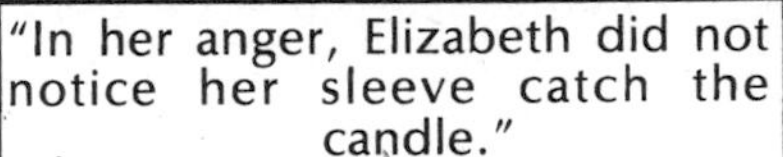
"In her anger, Elizabeth did not notice her sleeve catch the candle."

OH, NO! I'VE SET THE DOLLS' HOUSE ON FIRE! I MUST FIND SOMETHING WITH WHICH TO SMOTHER THE FLAMES BEFORE THEY SPREAD!

I'VE MANAGED TO PUT OUT THE FIRE, BUT I'M AFRAID THE TOP OF THE DOLLS' HOUSE IS DAMAGED. I HOPE MY UNCLE AND AUNT DON'T FIND OUT. I'LL GO TO BED NOW AND PULL THE COVER OVER MY HEAD AND HOPE TO SLEEP.

"Much later, when Elizabeth was asleep, the two servants returned."
OW! JUST BE CAREFUL WHO YOU'RE SHOVING, YOUNG NANCY!
I DIDN'T TOUCH YOU, MRS JENNINGS. DON'T PUSH! YOU'LL MAKE ME DROP MY CANDLE!

"The candle set the curtains on fire —"
BETTER GET OUT OF HERE! IF THERE'S A FIRE, WE'LL GET THE BLAME.
THAT'S RIGHT! WE WON'T STOP TO WAKE THE BRAT OR WE MIGHT BE SEEN LEAVING!

"The fire spread to Elizabeth's room —"
DON'T WORRY, CHILD, I'M COMING! YOU'LL BE SAFE IN A MOMENT! IS THERE ANYONE ELSE IN THE HOUSE?
N-NO! THERE WERE TWO SERVANTS, BUT I SAW THEM LEAVE A WHILE AGO!
SHAME! D'YOU HEAR THAT? THEY LEFT THE CHILD TO BURN!
"The story of the little girl who had been abandoned in a burning house got into the newspapers. One day, at the orphanage where Elizabeth had been taken —"
DEAR CHILD — I HAVE FOUND YOU AT LAST, THANKS TO THE NEWSPAPER STORY! I AM YOUR AUNT LUCY AND I HAVE BEEN SEARCHING FOR YOU EVER SINCE I CAME BACK TO THIS COUNTRY. I WILL BE DELIGHTED TO OFFER YOU A HOME WITH MYSELF AND MY HUSBAND AND SONS! I HAVE ALWAYS WANTED A DAUGHTER!
FOUNDED IN 18
WHAT A WEIRD STORY, GRAN! DO YOU REALLY THINK ELIZABETH MADE THOSE BAD THINGS HAPPEN TO HER AUNT AND UNCLE AND THE HOUSE, OR WAS IT THE DOLLS — OR JUST COINCIDENCE? WAS ELIZABETH A WITCH, LIKE HER GRANNY?
TAMSIN, M'DEAR — WHAT A LOT OF QUESTIONS!
NO, OF COURSE ELIZABETH WASN'T A WITCH! ALTHOUGH SHE DID TELL ME, WHEN WE WENT TO SCHOOL TOGETHER LATER, THAT SHE THOUGHT SOME POWER OR OTHER MIGHT HAVE COME TO HER AID WHEN SHE WAS SO UNHAPPY. BUT NOTHING LIKE THAT EVER HAPPENED AGAIN.
I WOULDN'T LIKE TO GUESS WHETHER IT WAS A COINCIDENCE OR NOT THAT WHEN ELIZABETH TOOK HER ANGER OUT ON THE DOLLS AN ACCIDENT BEFELL ONE OF THE HOUSEHOLD AFTERWARDS. BUT, JUST TO BE SAFE, I DON'T THINK I'LL PUT ANY DOLLS IN THERE!
QUITE RIGHT, GRAN! I'VE SUDDENLY GONE OFF THE IDEA OF PLAYING WITH TOYS. I'LL GO AND WATCH TV — IT'S SAFER!

The Flights of Flopear
TESSA WORTH had an unusual toy rabbit named Flopear which was really a highly-powered space craft in which she could travel. However, on the day before Christmas Eve, Tessa wanted to go no further than the High Street!
I FEAR I SHALL NEVER UNDERSTAND YOU EARTHLINGS! WHY DO YOU GET SO EXCITED ABOUT CHRISTMAS? IT'S JUST LIKE ANY OTHER DAY OF THE YEAR!
OH, NO IT'S NOT, FLOPEAR. WAIT TILL TONIGHT WHEN WE DECORATE THE TREE. THEN TOMORROW WHEN WE ALL GET OUR GIFTS, AND HAVE A SUPER MEAL! IT'S GREAT!
But, that night—
CHRISTMAS EVE! WHAT A NIGHT TO HAVE TO WORK LATE!
NEVER MIND, YOU'RE HOME AT LAST! DID YOU LEAVE THE TREE OUTSIDE?
TREE? OH, NO! I CLEAN FORGOT ABOUT IT! I'D BETTER SEARCH AROUND TOWN AND SEE IF THERE ARE ANY LEFT.

YOU'LL DO NO SUCH THING! YOU'RE COLD AND TIRED — AND ANYWAY, ALL THE SHOPS CLOSED HOURS AGO. WE'LL JUST DO WITHOUT A TREE THIS YEAR.
I'M SORRY! I'VE COMPLETELY RUINED CHRISTMAS!
POOR DAD FEELS AWFUL ABOUT FORGETTING THE TREE — BUT PERHAPS WE CAN STILL FIND ONE. FLOPEAR, WE'RE TAKING A TRIP.
NOW? WHAT IS YOUR DESTINATION?

ALL THE SHOPS MAY BE CLOSED HERE IN TOWN, BUT SURELY SOMEWHERE IN SPACE THERE'S A PLANET WITH A CHRISTMAS TREE TO SPARE?

Flopear was much bigger inside than out—
LOOK IN YOUR PLANET DATA-FILE, AND SEE WHERE THERE ARE LOTS OF TREES, FLOPEAR.
THE PLANET ARBOREUM ANSWERS THAT DESCRIPTION. I SUPPOSE I SHALL GET NO PEACE UNTIL I AGREE TO THIS RIDICULOUS IDEA!

So, far above the heads of carol singers, and over the snowy rooftops, Flopear left the Earth faster than the eye could follow—

And soon—
SO THIS IS THE PLANET ARBOREUM! IT'S COVERED IN TREES! WE'RE BOUND TO FIND A CHRISTMAS TREE HERE.

THIS ONE IS NOTHING LIKE A CHRISTMAS TREE.

AND THAT ONE ISN'T VERY FESTIVE-LOOKING.

OH, THESE ARE PERFECT! I WON'T BE GREEDY. I'LL JUST PULL UP A VERY TINY ONE.

But, as she approached it—
OH — IT'S SHOT BACK UNDERGROUND!

THEY'RE ALL DOING IT!
I HAVE RECEIVED FURTHER DATA ABOUT ARBOREUM! IT IS A TREE-CONSERVANCY PLANET. EACH TREE HAS THIS SPECIAL PROTECTIVE ACTION IF IT IS THREATENED WITH BEING UPROOTED OR DAMAGED.

WE MUST TRY SOMEWHERE ELSE, FLOPEAR. ALL I WANT IS A TINY LITTLE TREE THAT NO-ONE WOULD REALLY MISS.
THIS IS THE PLANET XENOBINA.
WHAT LOVELY WOODS! I'M BOUND TO FIND A LITTLE CHRISTMAS TREE HERE. LET'S EXPLORE!
W-WHAT'S GOING ON? THE TREES ARE WALKING!
XENOBINA IS FAMOUS FOR ITS SELF-PROPELLING TREES.
A CHRISTMAS TREE FROM HERE WOULDN'T BE MUCH GOOD! MUM WOULD HAVE A FIT IF SHE FOUND IT TAKING A STROLL AROUND OUR SITTING-ROOM!
ASK YOUR COMPUTER TO DIRECT US TO A PLANET WITH PLENTY OF ICE AND SNOW. THAT'S WHERE WE'LL FIND A CHRISTMAS TREE.
ARE YOU TELLING ME HOW TO DO MY JOB, EARTHLING?
The name that came up on Flopear's computer was 'Frio XL5'.
TAKE CARE WHEN WE LAND EARTHLING. FRIO XL FIVE IS TOO COLD EVER TO HAVE BEEN INHABITED.

WHOOPS! THIS IS ICE!
But then—
THESE ARE NOT ACTUALLY TREES, TESSA, BUT STRANGE ICE-FORMATIONS WHICH HAVE BEEN FORMED OVER HUNDREDS OF YEARS.
HOW BEAUTIFUL! BUT IF THEY'RE ONLY ICE, THEN I CAN'T TAKE ONE BACK TO EARTH.
CORRECTION! THEY HAVE BEEN SO DEEPLY FROZEN OVER THE CENTURIES, THAT EVEN IN THE WARMTH OF YOUR OWN PLANET, THEY WOULD NOT MELT FOR MANY WEEKS.
TO REMOVE IT, WE SIMPLY SLICE THROUGH THE 'TRUNK' WITH MY LASER BEAM.
THANKS FLOPEAR! NOW LET'S HURRY BACK TO EARTH. I CAN'T WAIT TO SEE MUM AND DAD'S FACES WHEN THEY FIND OUT WE HAVE A TREE AFTER ALL!
MUM AND DAD ARE IN THE KITCHEN. I MANAGED TO SMUGGLE THE TREE IN WITHOUT THEM SEEING!

THERE — ALL DONE! DOESN'T IT LOOK JUST PERFECT?
I REALLY CAN'T SEE WHAT ALL THE FUSS IS ABOUT — BUT AT LEAST YOU'RE HAPPY AT LAST!

POOR OLD FLOPEAR, YOU STILL HAVEN'T GOT THE CHRISTMAS SPIRIT, HAVE YOU? WAIT UNTIL I TURN OUT THE LIGHT, AND THEN YOU'LL REALLY SEE HOW LOVELY THE TREE LOOKS!

THE GLOW FROM THE FIRE DANCES IN ALL THE LITTLE ICE-LEAVES! IT'S — IT'S FANTASTIC!

And outside—
HEY — LOOK AT THAT AMAZING TREE IN THE WORTHS' WINDOW!
LET'S STOP AND GIVE THEM A CAROL IN ITS HONOUR.

O, CHRISTMAS TREE, O, CHRISTMAS TREE, HOW PRETTY ARE YOUR BRANCHES—

DON'T YOU FEEL THE CHRISTMAS MAGIC NOW, FLOPEAR? AS SOON AS I HEARD THE CAROL SINGERS IT SWEPT RIGHT OVER ME!
I MUST ADMIT I HAVE A STRANGE FLUTTERY FEELING ABOUT HERE, JUST TO THE LEFT OF MY MULTI-PURPOSE CIRCUIT-BREAKER.

WHAT ARE YOU DOING TO OUR LOVELY TREE?
I HAVE A SUDDEN IRRATIONAL DESIRE TO PRESENT YOU WITH A GIFT, TO CELEBRATE THIS UNUSUAL OCCASION.
YOU'VE MADE SOME OF THE ICE-LEAVES FALL ON MY DRESS!
OH, THANK YOU, FLOPEAR! YOU'VE TURNED MY OLD FROCK INTO A SUPER PARTY DRESS. WHAT A LOVELY PRESENT!
TESSA — WHERE DID YOU FIND SUCH A BEAUTIFUL TREE? WE'VE BROUGHT THE CAROL SINGERS IN TO TAKE A CLOSER LOOK.
YOU'D NEVER BELIEVE ME IF I TOLD YOU — SO LET'S JUST ENJOY IT.
I STILL THINK THIS HUMAN BEHAVIOUR IS COMPLETELY ILLOGICAL — BUT HAPPY CHRISTMAS ANYHOW!

COBBER THE KOALA

THE scruffy koala bear staggered along the verge of the highway. Normally he would not have ventured near a road, but a great forest fire had forced him on and on, in his efforts to escape the smoke and flames.

Now he was tired and dazed. He couldn't remember when he had last eaten. The eucalyptus trees with their fragrant, juicy leaves had been turned to black sticks by the flames. The cub was starving, his fur singed, his paws cut and bleeding.

Presently he could go no further and collapsed in a heap, barely alive.

Powerful cars swished past on the road, but he neither heard nor saw them, and none of the drivers noticed the koala curled up helplessly on the burnt grass. The first to spot him was Debbie, seated in the back of her parents' car.

"Look, Dad! There's a koala — and it's just a cub! Please stop!" she shouted.

"It'd be a waste of time," her Dad objected. "It can't have survived. And if it has, what would we do with it? You have more than enough pets at home already. Koalas belong in the outback."

But presently he gave way to Debbie's pleading and turned the car, taking a circular route which brought them back to where she had seen the cub.

She got out of the car and ran to where the animal lay. He was too tired even to feel fear, although he had never before been picked up and cuddled.

"It's alive," Debbie called triumphantly as she brought the koala back in her arms.

"But you can't keep it," her Dad reminded her. "And where can it go, even if it's not badly hurt? Best thing we can do is find a vet when we get to the next township. He may know of somewhere, but I wouldn't bank on it. There's no forest land left around here."

But to Debbie's relief the vet knew of a safe place for her find.

"The little chap isn't seriously hurt," he assured her. "He'll recover with the proper treatment. Then I'll take him over to the Koala Sanctuary. These cubs are very popular with tourists.

"Easy now, cobber," he murmured, gently swabbing the koala's cuts clean.

The vet called most of his animal patients "cobber", meaning friend, but without knowing it he had given the cub its name.

"THAT koala you found is such a friendly little fellow we tell the tourists his name is Cobber," said the warden in charge of the sanctuary when Debbie visited it months later.

She would hardly have known Cobber! His fur was soft and velvety, all trace of the fire damage gone, his body plump, and his eyes bright.

"Tourists pay to have their photographs taken with him," the warden told Debbie. "It makes a great souvenir of Australia. And look here."

He showed her shiny postcards of Cobber climbing a eucalyptus tree.

"Those are sent all over the world," he said. "Cobber's famous, not only for his looks but for his sweet nature."

"I'm sorry to leave you," Debbie murmured, dropping a kiss on his smooth, round head. "You're exactly like a real, live teddy bear. But at least I now have a picture of us together."

When she got home, Debbie framed the photograph and placed it on a chest of drawers in her room, so that she would always see Cobber's friendly face when she went to bed at night, and woke up in the morning.

January					
Su. ..		4	11	18	25
M. ..		5	12	19	26
Tu. ..		6	13	20	27
W. ..		7	14	21	28
Th. ..	1	8	15	22	29
F. ..	2	9	16	23	30
S. ..	3	10	17	24	31

February				
Su. ..	1	8	15	22
M. ..	2	9	16	23
Tu. ..	3	10	17	24
W. ..	4	11	18	25
Th. ..	5	12	19	26
F. ..	6	13	20	27
S. ..	7	14	21	28

March					
Su. ..	1	8	15	22	29
M. ..	2	9	16	23	30
Tu. ..	3	10	17	24	31
W. ..	4	11	18	25	
Th. ..	5	12	19	26	
F. ..	6	13	20	27	
S. ..	7	14	21	28	

April					
Su. ..		5	12	19	26
M. ..		6	13	20	27
Tu. ..		7	14	21	28
W. ..	1	8	15	22	29
Th. ..	2	9	16	23	30
F. ..	3	10	17	24	
S. ..	4	11	18	25	

May						
Su. ..		3	10	17	24	31
M. ..		4	11	18	25	
Tu. ..		5	12	19	26	
W. ..		6	13	20	27	
Th. ..		7	14	21	28	
F. ..	1	8	15	22	29	
S. ..	2	9	16	23	30	

June					
Su. ..		7	14	21	28
M. ..	1	8	15	22	29
Tu. ..	2	9	16	23	30
W. ..	3	10	17	24	
Th. ..	4	11	18	25	
F. ..	5	12	19	26	
S. ..	6	13	20	27	

July					
Su. ..		5	12	19	26
M. ..		6	13	20	27
Tu. ..		7	14	21	28
W. ..	1	8	15	22	29
Th. ..	2	9	16	23	30
F. ..	3	10	17	24	31
S. ..	4	11	18	25	

August						
Su. ..		2	9	16	23	30
M. ..		3	10	17	24	31
Tu. ..		4	11	18	25	
W. ..		5	12	19	26	
Th. ..		6	13	20	27	
F. ..		7	14	21	28	
S. ..	1	8	15	22	29	

September					
Su. ..		6	13	20	27
M. ..		7	14	21	28
Tu. ..	1	8	15	22	29
W. ..	2	9	16	23	30
Th. ..	3	10	17	24	
F. ..	4	11	18	25	
S. ..	5	12	19	26	

October					
Su. ..		4	11	18	25
M. ..		5	12	19	26
Tu. ..		6	13	20	27
W. ..		7	14	21	28
Th. ..	1	8	15	22	29
F. ..	2	9	16	23	30
S. ..	3	10	17	24	31

November					
Su. ..	1	8	15	22	29
M. ..	2	9	16	23	30
Tu. ..	3	10	17	24	
W. ..	4	11	18	25	
Th. ..	5	12	19	26	
F. ..	6	13	20	27	
S. ..	7	14	21	28	

December					
Su. ..		6	13	20	27
M. ..		7	14	21	28
Tu. ..	1	8	15	22	29
W. ..	2	9	16	23	30
Th. ..	3	10	17	24	31
F. ..	4	11	18	25	
S. ..	5	12	19	26	

Snow in Summer

THIS pretty Victorian snowstorm in a glass globe makes a great Christmas gift. And when summer comes again, just looking at the swirling snow during a heatwave makes you feel cool and refreshed!

YOU WILL NEED: Miniature Christmas cake decorations, e.g., a Santa, fir tree, Eskimos on a sledge, or a robin.

Strong, waterproof adhesive.

A glass jar with a screw-on lid, such as an empty hair-gel jar or honey pot.

Two dessertspoonfuls of dessicated coconut (all supermarkets sell it) OR a phial of Christmas snow glitter (from most big stores).

TO MAKE:

1. Wash out the jar and let it dry thoroughly.
2. Coat the bases of the Christmas cake decorations with strong, waterproof adhesive, and stick them to the bottom of the inside of the perfectly clean glass jar. This can be a bit tricky, but holding each ornament in place with a pair of eyebrow tweezers till the adhesive sticks is a big help.
3. Add the phial of snow glitter, or the dessicated coconut (which looks more like real snow).
4. Fill the jar to the top with water, or vinegar if you are using coconut for the snow.
5. Coat the inside of the rim of the lid with adhesive, so that when screwed on it sticks and stays in place.

N.B. GIVE THE CHRISTMAS CAKE DECORATIONS PLENTY OF TIME TO STICK FIRMLY BEFORE ADDING THE VINEGAR OR WATER.

You now have a captive snow scene in a jar, and need only shake it to make the flakes swirl gently round the little figures grouped inside.

OUT
OF
ORDER